GUINNESS

HORSE TAILS

Valerie Porter

Editor: Honor Head
Design and Layout: Michael Morey
Picture Research: Anne Marshall

© Valerie Porter and Guinness Publishing Ltd, 1989

Published in Great Britain by Guinness Publishing Ltd,
33 London Road, Enfield, Middlesex

Typeset in 8 on 9 pt Itek Meridien
by Ace Filmsetting Ltd, Frome, Somerset
Printed and bound in Portugal by Printer Portuguesa

British Library Cataloguing in Publication Data

Porter, Valerie,
    Horse tails
    1. Horses
    I. Title
    599.72'5

    ISBN 0-85112-382-1

CONTENTS

IN THE BEGINNING

God first made Man. He thought better of it and made Woman. When he found time, he made the Horse, which has the courage and spirit of Man and the beauty and grace of Woman.

Brazilian saying

Once upon a time, an animal no bigger than a small dog browsed peacefully in the lush tropical forests of North America in an area that is now Wyoming. It had small, low-crowned teeth set in a short muzzle and it had several toes on each of its soft-padded feet. It had been around for a very long time, and 55 million years after its first appearance they gave it the grand name of *Hyracotherium*.

In Greek, a hyrax is a shrew (though in fact the hyrax is a primitive ungulate related to elephants and aardvarks) but this creature was a horse, the first of its kind and the ancestor of all other equids.

After about 37 million years as the sole equid species, this little animal found itself in the throes of a sudden evolutionary burst that produced at least a dozen different species of horse in America, more adapted to grazing the plains than browsing low forest bushes. Among all these new branches springing from the *Hyracotherium* root was a group which eventually outlived all the other branches (including those in other parts of the world which became extinct 38 million years ago) and developed gradually into the genus we know as *Equus*, a single-toed mammal which evolved about one or two million years ago and which in due course became the horses, ponies, asses and zebras of today. But in the cradle of North America all the horses were wiped out quite suddenly about 10,000 years ago and did not return until they were ferried across the ocean

Reconstruction in field museum in Chicago of three-toed horses, said to have lived in America 30 million years ago. (ILN)

by post-Columbian invaders and settlers from the other side of the Atlantic.

FAMILY TIES

The horse family is part of the ungulate order **Perissodactyla**. The ungulates are larger, terrestrial, herbivorous hoofed mammals in five orders and, as well as the Perissodactyla, they include primitive ungulates (elephants, hyraxes and the aardvark) and the even-toed order Artiodactyla (camelids, pigs, peccaries, hippopotamus, deer, giraffe, cattle, sheep, goats and antelope).

The order Perissodactyla, or odd-toed ungulates, includes only three families:

EQUIDAE
Asses, horses and zebras

TAPIRIDAE
Tapirs

RHINOCEROTIDAE
Rhinoceroses

THE FAMILY TODAY

THE HORSES now include only two species: the wild horse, *Equus ferus*, represented today by only Przewalski's horse, and the domesticated horse, *Equus caballus*, descended from *E. ferus*.

THE ASSES, in the subfamily Asinus, are divided into two geographical groups: the Asiatic asses and the African asses. All the wild African species are either extinct or nearly so, but the domesticated ass, *Equus asinus*, is believed to be descended from the African species and very soon it will be the only living African ass. The Asiatic asses include the hemiones or onagers and the kiang, and many are endangered.

THE ZEBRAS, in the subfamily Hippotigris, were of four species until the quagga was exterminated in the 1880s.

THE HYBRIDS include mainly the ass/horse combinations (mule and hinny) though there has been experimental breeding here and there, and now and again, between zebras and asses.

EQUINE HABITS

All the equids are ground-living: they neither climb trees nor burrow. They are more efficient at digesting proteins but less efficient at digesting and absorbing energy from their food than the even-toed ungulates like cattle, sheep and deer.

In particular, the equids are adapted for living in open country: they have acute sight, hearing and sense of smell; they move on their toes, flexing their backs as they run to gain a longer, energy-efficient stride. Running is their main defence in the face of danger, and their first instinct is to escape and to keep within the herd while they do so. Only if cornered do they resort to using their hooves and teeth to protect themselves. They prefer to keep sufficiently far away from potential danger to feel comfortable, and if they cannot easily remove themselves from danger they panic. (It has been said that horse-racing is a form of controlled panic.) Once running, they need to run out their fright before stopping their headlong flight, and their young must be able to move with the fleeing herd within hours of birth.

Nearly all the equids are social by nature and hate to be alone, especially the onagers or hemiones. The normal social structure is non-territorial but with a male gathering a family group of as many females (and their young) as he can. Younger males live together in a separate group until each can steal some juvenile females to start his own family. Within a group, there is a well-established hierarchy: each animal knows its place and very

Przewalski's Horse. (Hulton)

often it is the most dominant female who leads the herd to new areas, with others following in order of dominance and with the male bringing up the rear.

There are two exceptions to this social behaviour. Grevy's zebra and the African wild ass are species of the desert and desert-steppe, where water and grazing are scarce, and the sexes tend to live separately for most of the year, with no permanent bonds between adults. Individuals might spend the day solitarily or might join with a random group of other individuals as the mood takes them.

PRZEWALSKI'S HORSE

The only truly wild horse still alive today is **Przewalski's Horse** (*Equus ferus przewalskii*).

Colonel Przewalski was a Russian explorer who discovered an unknown wild Mongolian horse in 1881 in the Tachin Schara Nuru mountains at the edge of the Gobi desert, an environment which is at the very extreme of any horse's range. The Mongolians called the horse Taki and it is possible that Mongolian, Tibetan and Chinese ponies today are its descendants: they share many of its characteristics, and Genghis Khan's formidable hordes probably rode very similar animals.

It is stocky, powerfully built and very tough, with a big heavy head, short neck, wide chest, almost no withers, and a rather puny back end. Its strong, short legs have the typical 'zebra' stripes of primitive horses and its hooves are large and flat. Its mane characteristically sticks up as if it had been hogged and there is no forelock. It has a mealy muzzle and eye rings, like the Exmoor, and its coat is generally various shades of dun or dark bay. There is a black stripe running the length of the back, and sometimes an ass-like shoulder stripe. The mane and tail are dark, and the hairs on the upper half of the tail are short while those on the lower half are long.

Twenty years after the Colonel's discovery, a world-famous collector of exotic animals who ran huge travelling animal shows (in which human natives were exhibited like any other exotic animal) decided to capture specimens of this last of the wild horses. The flamboyant Karl Hagenbeck commandeered two thousand Kirghis tribesmen and they rounded up 32 young horses for him. The animals took readily to captivity and soon began to breed. Today their descendants are in many zoos and Marwell Zoo in Hampshire has a breeding scheme which has been so successful that some of the horses are being returned to the wild in their native habitat where the original wild herds are virtually extinct.

THE TARPAN'S TALE

The Tarpan, *Equus ferus gmelini*, was either a wild horse or a domesticant which reverted to the wild in ancient times. Like the Exmoor, it is a very ancient type and they are probably both descended from feral ponies.

The Tarpan looked very like the wild Przewalski's horse of Mongolia in many ways and was possibly a natural hybrid between the Celtic and western Asian types of pony. It used to run free in eastern Europe and western Russia but the last free Tarpan died in 1879 near Askania Nova, having escaped from a Polish herd and been pursued until it broke its leg. In 1919 the last Tarpan in captivity also died and the species was extinct. However, many Poles had habitually captured wild ponies and many had animals that at least

The Tarpan. (Hulton)

still resembled the original Tarpan. A Polish breeding scheme reconstructed the breed with the help of the look-alikes, and now several forest herds of the New Tarpan run semi-wild in Polish reserves. A steppe Tarpan has been recreated by putting Przewalski stallions to Konik mares.

Tarpans were usually mouse-dun, ash grey or brown, with short, erect, dark manes and rather short, dark tails, dark stockings, zebra-striped legs and a black eelstripe along the spine. Occasionally they would grow white hairs in their winter coats (which gave better camouflage in a snowy landscape).

Some say that the Tarpan was the basis of all the horses of the chariot-driving nations in the eastern Mediterranean, from Hittites to Greeks, and of the peasant ponies of east central Europe and the Balkans. Certainly the first domesticated horses looked very like the Tarpan and, like the original breed and the Przewalski, they all had short, erect manes.

RUNNING WILD

There are lots of feral herds scattered throughout the world but they are not wild horses. They are descended from the domestic horse, having escaped or been released from man's total control, and are living and breeding freely, though many of the herds are rounded up at regular intervals for branding and culling, or for capture of the young, or are being persecuted out of existence because they are considered as pests. Here are some of those that run free:

ASSATEAGUE AND CHINCOTEAGUE These are two small uninhabited islands off the coast of Maryland and Virginia in the United States where ponies run wild apart from an annual round-up in July, when those on Assateague are swum across to Chincoteague

(they swim back again if they are not sold). Like many island ponies, legend has it that they are survivors of a shipwreck in colonial times. They are extremely tough, surviving without shelter and on marshy grazing and scrub.

BRUMBY The first horses – a stallion, three mares and two fillies – landed in Australia in 1788 and promptly escaped into the bush. By 1798 there were 117 horses in the colony, by the early 1820s there were 5,000, and at the turn of the century more than 16,000 were found for regiments joining the Boer War, In the First World War more than 121,000 well-bred Walers went to war.

Like other introduced animals in Australia, horses escaped or were abandoned and ran wild and, like rabbits, dingoes, camels and kangaroos, they were generally regarded as pests to be exterminated. Australia's wild horses, known as brumbies, still try and live in the Northern Territory's deserts and mountains but it is a losing battle for them and, in spite of their hardiness and cunning, their numbers have been severely reduced by relentless culling: long gone are the days when they numbered 200,000.

CAMARGUE The white horses of the Camargue in southern France's Rhône delta marshes are used traditionally for herding black bulls destined for the bullring. They are horses of the sea, running free for much of the time on the marshes and surviving on tough, salty marsh grasses.

CRIOLLO The youngstock of these South American descendants of the conquistador horses used to run wild over huge areas and were rounded up with the help of special mares known as madrinas. The mares wore bells around their necks, each with a different tone, and each had a tropilla, or troop of ponies who would stay near their own madrina, always grazing close by and following her.

DÜLMEN The Dülmen ponies are a single, semi-wild herd on the Duke of Croy's estate at Meerfelder Bruch in Westphalian Munsterland, where they have run since the 14th century. They are rounded up annually so that surplus stock can be sold and, along with the almost extinct Senner, they are the only native pony breeds in Germany.

EXMOOR The Exmoor ponies are unique in that they are the only ones in the world to show the same type of jaw development as that found in fossilized Alaskan bones of the original 'Celtic' ponies dating back a hundred thousand years. They have heavily lidded 'toad' eyes and a distinctive 'ice' tail (very thick, with a fan-like growth at the top) and mealy muzzle like the wild Przewalski. They wander freely over the moors all year and are self-sufficient survivors but each belongs to someone and carries a brandmark. Traditionally they are rounded up for sale at the annual Bampton Fair, but they are now quite rare and carefully conserved.

GALICIAN The Galician pony is a semi-feral type in north-west Spain, whence it was exported to Mexico in the 16th century (where it is known as the Galiceno). Like other Celtic types, it is ancient and very hardy but is now in need of protection to prevent its extinction.

GOWER On the Gower peninsula in south Wales about 500 Welsh mountain ponies run free on the commons, as they have since time immemorial. Welsh mountain ponies were found here at the time of the Roman invasion in 55 BC and they so impressed Julius Caesar that he formed the first stud at Bala in Merionethshire, Wales, improving the native pony with Arab blood. More than a thousand years later

the Crusaders brought in Arab stallions to produce the typical Welsh mountain pony of today with its bright, prominent eyes, dished face and small, pricked ears.

The herds were still living free on the mountains after Henry VIII passed legislation in 1535 insisting that stallions used for breeding throughout his kingdom must be at least 14 hands high (hh) (his heavily armoured soldiers needed strong mounts) and this was increased to 15 hands eight years later, but the message never reached the Welsh hills! Most of the Gower peninsula ponies are still less than 12 hh.

KAIMANAWA This 'wild' horse of New Zealand's North Island is feral and rare and fast going the way of the brumby.

MUSTANG The feral horses and cow ponies of America are basically descended from the Spanish conquistador animals, whether they are called broomtails, Indian ponies, cimarrons, criollos, barbs or mustangs. For generations they were the plentiful stock from which ranchers picked new saddle and draught animals at will, and serious mustangers would capture large numbers of them for the army at home and abroad. Later, they were a valuable source of dog-meat and by 1970 all but about 20,000 had been 'canned'.

Then Velma Johnston of Reno, alias Wild Horse Annie, came to their rescue to reduce the slaughter and Congress passed an act in 1971 which has since led to a tripling of their numbers in the wild. There is a public Adopt-a-Horse programme, and long-term inmates in prisons in Colorado and New Mexico are trying to tame some of the more intractable beasts. There are also horseback seminars on the ecology of mustang herds, and dude branding round-ups for tourists.

The word mustang comes from

the Spanish *mestengo*, an unbranded feral horse, and the Western buckaroo or *vaquero* riding the range can trace his style of horsemanship back to old Spain and thence to the Moors, Arabia, the Tartars and the Mongols of the Asian steppes.

NEW FOREST The familiar New Forest ponies of England wander freely on their Hampshire commons but are regularly rounded up for branding and for the Beaulieu Road sales. They are something of a mixture as all sorts of breeds have been introduced to the Forest over the centuries in order to improve the basic stock – Welsh ponies, Dartmoors and Exmoors, Highlands, Fells and Dales, Hackneys, Arabs and even Clydesdales and the Thoroughbred stallion Marske, sire of the famous 18th century racehorse Eclipse.

SABLE ISLAND Feral ponies have been running free on this Canadian island since at least 1739. The island is really no more than a sandbank 200 miles off Nova Scotia and it is difficult to understand why these French ponies should have been introduced there, where they exist on very poor grazing – vegetation is sparse and there are no trees. But about three hundred of them are tough enough to survive.

DOMESTICATION

There are endless and ever-changing theories on the evolution of the horse and the same applies to the history of its domestication. When an animal is domesticated, humans control its breeding to such an extent that its form gradually alters to suit human purposes, and many people have tried to categorize the different forms. In 1907 J Cosser Ewart settled for four primitive types having survived the Ice Age:

FOREST HORSE heavily built and solid, with a big, heavy head, living in northern Europe and sometimes called the NORSE HORSE. Founder of the 'cold-blood' breeds, i.e. heavy draught types.

STEPPE HORSE finer, more lightly built pony about 12 hh, from Asia and north Africa. Ancestor of the oriental 'hot-blood' breeds such as the Arab.

PLATEAU HORSE originating in Siberia and the north of Asia and Europe. Joint ancestor with the Steppe of the 'warm-blood' breeds like the Thoroughbred.

TUNDRA HORSE not much influence on anything, except perhaps the Yakut horse of polar regions.

Another way of looking at the post-glacial types available for domestication is as follows:

CELTIC OR ATLANTIC PONY (e.g. Exmoor, Icelandic)

NORSE HORSE of northern Eurasia (e.g. Fjord, Noriker, Highland)

CENTRAL ASIAN HORSE (e.g. Sorraia, Akhal-Teke, Karabakh, evolving through to Turkomene and Andalusian types)

WEST ASIAN PONY (the Caspian)

PRZEWALSKI'S HORSE in a category of its own. The Tarpan, according to this system, is a combination of the first and fourth types, at a point where their ranges overlap.

In geographical terms, animals tend to adapt to the local climate and at northern latitudes they become more thickset, standing on relatively short legs, and keeping their extremities such as ears quite small as protection against the cold. At lower latitudes and in warmer climates they generally have longer, finer limbs and longer ears. The northern species, adapted to temperate seasons, grow good thick coats in winter, whereas more southerly horses have a short, sleek coat all year round. On this basis, there are probably three categories:

1 The small, stocky ponies of northern and central Europe.
2 Heavy horses of northern and central Europe.
3 Slim-limbed Arabian types in the south.

During the Bronze Age, domestication began to emphasize the differences between these geographical types.

POSSIBLE CHRONOLOGY OF DOMESTICATION

Large herds of wild horses grazed the open grasslands throughout Eurasia from 30,000 to 10,000 years ago and were hunted by man for food. They were depicted in many cave-paintings, for example at Lascaux and in the Altamira caves at Santillana del Mar. About 10,000 years ago all the wild equids in North America completely disappeared, and by 8000 BC very few herds of wild horses remained in north and west Europe after the last Ice Age: forests took over the landscape, which is not a good environment for horses.

3000 BC Domestication of the horse probably began during the 3rd millennium (possibly earlier in China) in a region north east of the Mediterranean stretching towards the Bering Straits and perhaps as far as Siberia. Plenty of pictorial evidence of domesticated donkeys and horses in western Asia early in the millenium. Mules common by 2500 'BC.

2000 BC Evidence of remains of horses throughout Europe, from Greece to the Orkneys. Numbers increasing hugely during Bronze Age. Domestication achieved by late Bronze Age even in the Northern Isles.

1600 BC First definitive records of riding, depicted on the tomb of

Horenhab in Egypt, but also mentioned in the time of Hammurabi *c.* 2000 BC.

1400 BC Earliest significant written text – a chariot-training manual by Kikkulis the Mittanite.

430 BC Birth of Xenophon, the great writer on horsemanship (died 354 BC).

AD 477 First mention of stirrups in literature.

THE OLD TESTAMENT

'The earliest record of the Horse which we possess is in the Old Testament, where we first find him inferentially mentioned in the thirty-sixth chapter of Genesis, as existing in the wilderness of Idumea about the beginning of the sixteenth century before Christ. Many commentators, however, render the word which is translated "mules" in our version, as "waters", and thus a doubt is thrown upon the correctness of the inference which is thence drawn. Moreover, in the thirty-second chapter of Genesis, camels, goats, sheep, cattle and asses are all severally alluded to, but no horses.' ['Stonehenge' (J H Walsh, FRCS, editor of *The Field*) in his comprehensive book on *The Horse*, 1862].

Genesis 36, v24 *'And these are the children of Zibeon; both Ajah, and Anah: this was that Anah that found the mules in the wilderness, as he fed the asses of Zibeon his father.'*

As a mule is the progeny of ass and mare, the horse had to be domesticated to produce the mule. In due course the horse was portrayed in all his might in Job 39, vv19–25, beginning:

'Hast thou given the horse strength? Hast thou clothed his neck with thunder? Canst thou make him afraid as a grasshopper? The glory of his nostrils is terrible. He paweth in the valley, and rejoiceth in his strength; he goeth on to

meet the armed men. He mocketh at fear, and is not affrighted; neither turneth he back from the sword.'

Jacob, on his death-bed, talks of the horse and its rider and, suggests 'Stonehenge', horses were present in large numbers in Egypt: Pharaoh is recorded as having taken 'six hundred chosen chariots, and all the horses' to pursue the Israelites to the Red Sea.

THE ANCIENT GREEKS

Many a Greek would have borne with pride the name Philip– meaning lover of horses. The Greeks equated horses with heroes, and the animals abound in Greek mythology. It was the Greeks who invented chariot racing; they also rode bareback much like the young men of Skyros ride their island ponies today. The famous Parthenon friezes show that the typical horse of the time was no more than a pony, and the riders' legs hang down almost to the ground on either side of their animals. Alexander the Great, who learned his riding from the Scythians, had horses so small that when he crossed the flooded Hydaspes channel, according to Arrian, 'the water at its deepest part was over the breasts of the men on foot; the horses could keep only their heads above the river'.

THE PONIES OF SKYROS Today's tiny, fine-boned ponies on the Greek island of Skyros are no more than 9–11 hh. The half-wild animals have large heads, large nostrils, wide intelligent eyes, powerfully muscular necks, strong wiry legs, slightly sway backs, rather big bellies, cow-hocked quarters, and very thick, low-set tails which reach almost to the ground. If you compare them to the Parthenon steeds of the 5th century BC, the likeness is striking. There is also a strong resemblance to the old Tarpan in the long ears, narrow

shoulders, dark mane and eelstripe, but today's Skyros ponies have very long, shaggy manes rather than the upright crest of the Tarpan, and their coat colours are quite different.

XENOPHON (430–354 BC) A general and historian but above all a horseman and author of a treatise on horses and horsemanship, Xenophon's advice was followed by Philip of Macedon (father of Alexander the Great) and has been highly rated by horsemen ever since. Much of his advice still holds good today, and perhaps the following are apposite:

'Riders who force their horses by the use of the whip only increase their fear, for they then associate the pain with the thing that frightens them.'

'It must be realized that spirit in a horse is precisely what anger is in a man. Therefore, just as you are least likely to make a man angry if you neither say nor do anything disagreeable to him, so he who abstains from annoying a spirited horse is least likely to rouse his anger.'

'If you reward him with kindness when he has done what you wish and admonish him when he disobeys, he will be most likely to do what you want. This holds good in every branch of horsemanship.'

Xenophon, in the style of his time, preferred to ride bare-legged so that his calves and thighs were in direct contact with his mount: he felt safer like that in an age when the stirrup was apparently unknown and even a back-cloth unusual, let alone a saddle. This is how he described the correct seat:

'When he has taken his seat, whether on the horse's bare back or on a cloth, we do not like that he should sit as if he were on a carriage seat, but as if he were standing upright with his legs somewhat apart; for thus he will cling more firmly to the horse with his thighs, and, keeping himself erect, he will be able to throw a javelin or to strike a blow on horseback, if it be necessary, with greater force.'

The launching of a weapon in the style of Xenophon is beautifully portrayed on a sarcophagus frieze showing Alexander on Bucephalus attacking the Persian cavalry at the battle of Issus.

THE SCYTHIANS

Scythia was a kingdom just north of the Black Sea whose nomadic herdsmen adored horses. They were superb riders and excellent artists, though their animal depictions were somewhat stylized. The Scythian horses were larger than the Greek ponies and had a hint of the Arabian in their conformation. Large numbers of them were imported by the Greeks, often complete with riders, and Philip of Macedon seized 20,000 Scythian mares. The Scythians were centuries ahead of their time: they even used a rudimentary stirrup, no more than a metal hook on a metal chain (judging by a beautifully worked gold torque found in the Crimea). Neither the Greeks nor the Romans managed to invent stirrups, and it was left to the Chinese to start the trend several centuries later.

THE ROMANS

Alexander the Great did manage to capture some of the much taller Bactrian-type Nisaean horses when he conquered Persia, in order to continue upgrading the small Macedonian animals, but the Greek mounts were mostly about 12 hh and generally less than 14 hh. However, the Roman military steeds were more like horses, at more than 14 hh, and they spread all over the empire, as far north as Hadrian's Wall. But the Romans were nothing like as accomplished and natural horsemen as the Greeks and their cavalry was soon cut to pieces by the mounted troops of the barbarians. (They did not do much better with their elephants, either.)

HANS AND HUNS

At the beginning of the Christian era the Chinese were about to witness the fall of the Han dynasty and, judging from artistic representations of the period, their war chariots and horses were formidable. Indeed the threat of Chinese power was enough to make the nomadic tribes of central Asia head west rather than east, and among the first were the Huns, a race of equestrians.

Ammian the Greek described the Huns and their horses as terrifyingly ugly, saying that the men had crooked bodies and sat on their steeds as if nailed to them, that they lived on roots (though he also claimed they kept raw meat under their saddles to avoid the bother of cooking it) and that they had no culture and no religion other than a passion for gold.

Not true! The Huns had profound ideas on the nature of the universe; they excelled in military organization, diplomacy and strategy and, above all, they were superb equestrians. Their rough, bony horses had small heads, short strong legs and down-sloping backs but they could cover more than sixty miles a day over the deserts. Their riders were sustained with kumiss, a lightly fermented food made from mare's milk. They were true nomads, mobilized by horses – animals which other semi-nomadic races considered to be ornamental luxuries rather than essential means of transport. The Huns knew better,

16

Attila and mount on the march to Paris from a painting by Delaunay.
(Hulton)

and during his time of power in the mid-5th century AD Attila the Hun's horseborne hordes simply overran Europe.

ISLAM AND ARABIANS

Horses were important to the beginnings of Islamic legend and history. The prophet Mohammed (AD 570–632) demonstrated the value of the horse in war, and in legend he was given a fabulous steed named Al Borak, who ultimately bore him to heaven.

Horse-breeding soon became vital to the desert tribes and the Koran encouraged the faithful to breed foals in large numbers in order to swell the armies against the infidel. Arabian horse-breeding had originally been an occupation of the rich and powerful but, as a religious duty, it spread to others too and 'quality' became even more important than quantity. The world today can be eternally grateful for the quality of the Arabian horse. Their deep respect for horses is summed up in these two Arab sayings: 'If you hear that a chestnut has been seen to fly with wings, believe it.' And: 'The horse is God's gift to man.'

BACKWATER BRITAIN

The islands of Britain were protected by the sea but were invaded by various waves of early races like the Picts and Celts. The latter migrated in the first millennium BC, gathering horses as they moved from the Danube valley. Britain already had its own stocky, 'Celtic' type ponies before the Celts themselves arrived, but the newcomers were strongly orientated towards horses and even had a goddess of the horses called Epona. Pictish stone inscriptions showed ponies like those still found in the Hebrides, and the native ponies of the northern and western isles of Scotland, which had both Celtic and Norse invaders and colonizers, have much in common with the ponies of Iceland and the Faroes.

The people, personified in Boudicca, were efficient charioteers and riders by the time the Romans arrived. Then the Dark Ages descended and drew a black, impenetrable veil over the development of the British horse until it emerged stitched to the Bayeux tapestry and looking rather different from the sturdy little Celtic pony.

From then on armour became more and more cumbersome and the horses had to become bigger, broader and stronger to carry their knights. The day of the famous old English black war steed known as the Great Horse was dawning, with all its trappings of jousting, pageantry and chivalry. Chivalry: a word evocative of bravery and boldness combined with courtesy and gallantry, and a word with its roots in *caballus*, the Latin name for a horse.

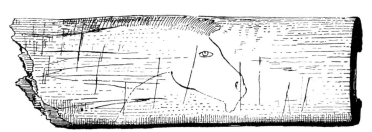

Engraved bone from Derbyshire, depicting a horse's head.

THE BREEDS

God, by a special interposition, directed to the ark the two most perfect animals then in existence, whence they found their way to Central Arabia, and their offspring, preserving their pure blood to this day, have sufficed to ennoble and improve the studs of the world.

Captain Upton, 19th century author, *Arabia and Newmarket*

According to the *World Dictionary of Livestock Breeds*, by I L Mason, there were nearly 500 breeds and types of horses and ponies in the world in 1988. In addition, the book lists about 90 breeds which have become extinct fairly recently, and suggests that about a score of today's breeds are nearly or probably extinct, while another 70 or so are very low in numbers and will probably disappear in the foreseeable future.

When J H Walsh ('Stonehenge') published his essential book *The Horse, in the Stable and the Field: His varieties, management in health and disease, anatomy, physiology, etc. etc.* in 1862, he devoted separate chapters to 'The Horses of the East', 'The Horses of the Western Hemisphere' (i.e. America), 'European Continental Horses', and three chapters of British horses. Not all the breeds he described still exist today.

THE STONEHENGE BREEDS

THE HORSES OF THE EAST

THE BARB, named after the area in which it was found (Tunis, Tripoli, Algiers, and Fez, on the north African Barbary coast) – slender, elegant and muscular, lower in size than the Arabs and with less spirit, speed or endurance.

THE EGYPTIAN HORSE, a very second-rate animal, 'ugly, of coarse shape, and looking more like a cart-horse than a racer' but with such an impetuosity that they were 'peculiarly desirable for heavy cavalry'.

THE DONGOLA was said to be of the highest symmetry, size and strength with an excellent temper and docility, but some travellers found fault with them for being 'deficient in stoutness'.

OTHER AFRICAN HORSES described by travellers included the BORNOU (superior to the Barb and Arab, said Mr Tully, but other travellers could not verify this), and the SOUTH AFRICAN horse used by the Kafirs in wars with the 'Boors' (a wiry and most useful animal but plain and unsightly).

THE MODERN ARAB, source of great controversy as to its stud value but gladly credited with the enormous value of its contribution to the English Thoroughbred, though 'how long it would take to bring a modern Arab, even of the highest caste, to the state of perfection of our own WEST AUSTRALIANS and STOCKWELLS it would be difficult to say'. There were six distinct breeds of Arabs: the DGELFE of Arabia Felix, remarkable for speed and fire yet 'mild as lambs', and able to go without food or water for a long time; the SECLAONI from the eastern part of the desert, looking quite like the lofty, long-eared Dgelfe but not so highly valued; the MEFKI of Damascus, handsome but not as swift as the first two breeds and looking more like an

Modern Arabian racehorse with its owner His Highness Sheik Al Khalafa. (Keystone)

ANDALUSIAN; the SABI, much like the Mefki; the very common FRIDI, which were often vicious and did not possess the excellent qualities of the other breeds; and the NEJDI, from the neighbourhood of Bussorah, which equalled or surpassed the Dgelfe and Seclaoni. These six breeds were described by Ali Bey, who quite failed to mention the KOCHLANI or KAILHAN descended from the stud of Mohammed, who was supposed to have laid the foundation of the Arabian pedigrees.

THE PERSIAN HORSES included several varieties, most with plenty

A Persian Charger. (Fotomas)

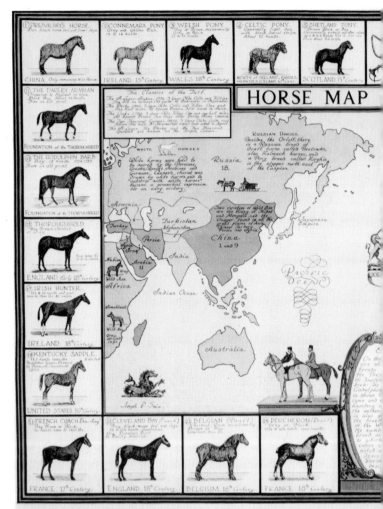

HORSE MAP

① PRJEVALSKY'S HORSE
CHINA. Only remaining Wild Horse

② CONNEMARA PONY
IRELAND. 13th Century

③ WELSH PONY
WALES 18th Century

④ CELTIC PONY
NORTH of IRELAND, FAROES, HEBRIDES, ICELAND 10th Cent.

⑤ SHETLAND PONY
SCOTLAND 15th Century

⑪ THE DARLEY ARABIAN
FOUNDATION of the THOROUGHBRED

⑬ THE GODOLPHIN BARB
FOUNDATION of the THOROUGHBRED

⑯ THOROUGHBRED
ENGLAND. Early 18th Century

⑰ IRISH HUNTER
IRELAND. 18th Century

⑲ KENTUCKY SADDLE
UNITED STATES 19th Century

㉑ FRENCH COACH
FRANCE. 17th Century

㉒ CLEVELAND BAY
ENGLAND. 18th Century

㉓ BELGIAN (Draft)
BELGIUM. 18th Century

㉔ PERCHERON (Draft)
FRANCE. 18th Century

The Classics of the Turf

RUSSIAN HORSES

Russia 18.

Armenia
Turkey
Turkistan
Afghanistan
Persia
Nubia
Iraq
Arabia 11.
Africa
India

China 1 and 9

Japanese Empire

Indian Ocean

Pacific Ocean

Australia

Joseph & Swin

"A HORSE MAP OF THE WORLD": THE COUNTRIES OF ORIGIN OF SOME THIRTY BREE

With the Grand National fresh in memory and sporting folk beginning to look forward to another Derby, the Briton's perennial interest in horseflesh is just now particularly strong. The time seems appropriate, therefore, to publish this delightful map, showing the various equine breeds and their countries of origin, and forming a companion picture to the "Dog Map of the World" given a year ago in our issue of March 2, 1935. As the racehorse and its descent are mainly in question at the moment, it may be interesting to add to the author's notes a few historical details concerning the famous "foundation" sires numbered 11 and 13 on the map. Writing in "The

Encyclopædia of Sport," the late Wilfred Scawen Blunt said: "The Arab horse in Arabic, *Keheilan*, is probably the most ancient of existing domestic breeds. He is also the original 'thoroughbred' horse of the East, from whom exemplar all Western ideas of thorough breeding in horseflesh were derived. He has been held in repute as of 'noble' blood for at least 1300 years. In England we first hear of 'Barbs' in Charles II.'s time, when the 'Royal Mares' were brought for the King from Tangiers, and about the same time of 'Turks,' captured in the wars in Hungary. It was not, however, till the beginning of the eighteenth century that the great success of the 'T

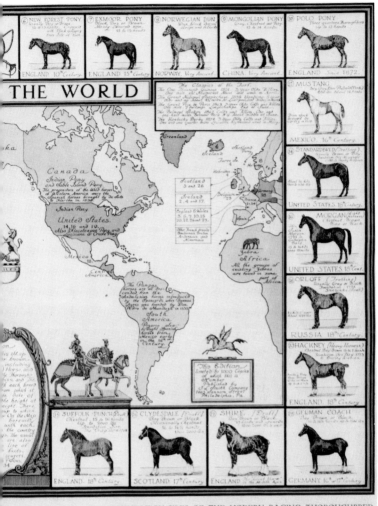

HORSES, INCLUDING THE FOUNDATION SIRES OF THE MODERN RACING THOROUGHBRED.

abian, a horse of undoubted Kehailan blood and purchased direct from the by whom he was presented to the Earl of Godolphin, whence his description :
abs of Northern Arabia by Mr. Darley, our Consul at Aleppo, revealed to he seems to have had no name. He laid the foundations of the family, and
glish breeders the true source of excellence in Eastern blood." In the according to further report pined away and died of remorse after accidentally
ne work another writer states : "The Godolphin Barb or Arabian was, a killing his favourite cat." The horse-map, like the dog-map above mentioned,
e brown horse he only stood about fifteen hands foaled in 1724. His origin was designed by Mr. Joseph P. Sims, a Philadelphia architect, who has occupied
doubtful, the rumour being that he was sent as a present by the Emperor himself for some years in decorative and historical cartography. The new
Morocco to Louis XIV. He is said to have been stolen and taken to horse-map, it should be mentioned, is also issued by the same firm of
ris, where he did the humblest possible duty in a water-cart. An English- American publishers, Messrs. J. L. Smith Co., of 1607, Sansom Street,
an, Mr. Coke, bought him for £3, and gave him to a Mr. Roger Williams. Philadelphia, U.S.A., and is reproduced here by special permission.

of Arabian blood. Those of the desert and country about Hillah were very small but 'full of bone, and of good speed'. And in Fars and Irak 'they have a mixed breed from the Arabian, which though stronger is still a small horse compared with either the TOORKOMAN or KHORASSAN breed, which are most prized by the soldiers of Persia'.

THE TURKISH HORSE was 'merely an Arab developed by higher food into a larger size and more massive proportions'.

THE HORSES OF TOORKISTAN were described as 'scanty in barrel, long in the leg, with ewe necks and large heads' but the cross with Persian horses produced a 'most magnificent animal, all elegance and elasticity'. There was also in Bokhara a breed of KUZZAK horses, small, sturdy, shaggy-coated, with very long manes and tails, and 'deservedly admired'. But the TARTAR horses were small and narrow, with long necks, weak legs, large heads and light middles; however, they were fast, untiring and very hardy, thriving on food which would starve even a donkey. Wild horses found in various parts of Tartary presented a 'rough inelegant form not unlike that of our NEW FOREST ponies' and they were thought to be one and the same as the domesticated Tartars: they were generally red, with a black stripe along the back, and the manes and tails were black with a reddish tinge at the roots of the dock and on the edges of the mane.

THE HORSES OF INDIA included the native BENGAL breeds ('Roman noses and sharp narrow foreheads, much white in their eyes, ill-shaped ears, square heads, thin necks, narrow chests, shallow girths, lank bellies, cat hams, goose rumps, and switch tails!') which were hardy and fleet, docile until they were four or five years old, after which 'their vice

is proverbial' for they were given to rearing, kicking, biting, and 'a thousand equally disagreeable habits', claimed Williamson in his *Wild Sports of the East.*

THE BIRMAN HORSE was very small, seldom more than 13 hh and sometimes less than 11; and the same applied to the horses of CHINA, SIAM and JAVA.

THE AUSTRALIAN HORSE in 'the Irishman's fifth quarter of the world' was admirable. Colonial-bred horses had been adapted for the turf and the road, as well as for agricultural work, and were 'superior in soundness and probably in stoutness, even if they are deficient in face, as compared with the British Thoroughbred'.

THE HORSES OF AMERICA

THE SOUTH AMERICAN HORSE was introduced by the Spaniards in 1535, according to Azara, and several more were shipped to Paraguay in 1537. 'From these have been bred the countless herds which have since spread over the whole southern part of the western world, and passing the Isthmus of Panama have wandered into North America.' Horses were there for the taking, in huge numbers, and Captain Head 'rode all across the continent from one shore to the other, nearly using up one horse in the course of fifty or sixty miles, and then looking out for another before the first was so spent as to be unable to assist him in making the exchange.'

THE MUSTANG, or Wild Horse of North America, found in Mexico and California, was also descended from Spanish blood. Large herds of INDIAN PONIES ran wild in the northern and north-western parts of the continent and were assumed to have the same origins as the Mustang. The Indian animal never exceeded 13 hh; it was remarkable for its activity and strength in spite of its size, 'appearing, like its Scotch congener, to be almost overwhelmed with its rider, whose feet nearly touch the ground, yet moving under its load with freedom.'

THE CANADIAN HORSE was about 14 to 15 hh, with shaggy fetlocks and a voluminous, massive mane falling on both sides of the neck in 'crimpled waves', a characteristic shared by the abundant tail; it was very hardy and able to travel very long distances but not more than average in speed. However, crossed with a Thoroughbred the Canadian produced the best of the American trotters with speed, endurance, and iron constitution and legs.

THE MORGAN HORSE had been kept pure in its own district since the early years of the century and was descended from 'a single horse, in the possession of Mr Justin Morgan, a schoolmaster in Vermont'. The founder of the family was got by a horse called True Briton (said to have been stolen and therefore of doubtful pedigree, but claimed to be the son of the English Thoroughbred, Traveller or Moreton's Old Traveller). This founder horse was about 14 hh; he was dark bay with black legs and no white hairs at all. His black mane and tail were coarse and heavy, with straight hair and not inclined to curl like that of the Canadian. His short legs were very muscular, and he had a noticeably fast walk but a slow, smooth trot with a vigorous, untiring action. His descendants included many famous fast trotters. By the 1860s the Morgan was 'very stout and enduring, with good action, especially in the trot, and great hardness of constitution'. He always had a thick, long mane and tail 'with a considerable curl in both' and a 'corky' frame.

THE AMERICAN TROTTER was not a distinct race, breed or family of horse, but many came from Canadian or Norman-French stock; others came from 'the ordinary undistinguished country horse of the southernmost of the midland states', or from the Vermont (Morgan) family, or from the Indian pony, or in part from the Thoroughbred. ('The low, lazy, lounging, daisy-cutting gait and action of the full-blooded horse of Oriental blood is not generally compatible with great trotting action or speed.')

THE NARRAGANSETT PACER was 'nearly or quite extinct'. It was a beautiful descendant of the Spanish horse, and was introduced into New England by Governor Robinson, from Andalusia, with reinforcements from Cuba for many years, but when carriages were introduced this natural pacer breed became neglected.

THE AMERICAN THOROUGH-BRED was descended from imported English Thoroughbreds, the first being Spark, imported by the Governor of Maryland (Mr Ogle) shortly before 1750. More than 200 English animals had been imported by the 1830s.

THE HORSES OF EUROPE

SPANISH AND PORTUGUESE HORSES had originally included a 'hardy and useful breed of horses, of different degrees of lightness and activity' but in both countries they had 'greatly degenerated from their former excellence'. The old breeds had owed much to Barbs imported by the Moors. The SPANISH JENNET had always been celebrated for 'easy paces and gentle temper', which had been the characteristics of all the Peninsular breeds, 'united in most of them with a high courage which would induce them to face either the dangers of war or a bull-fight without flinching'.

Spanish.

THE ITALIAN HORSE was supposed to be descended from the Barb but had greatly degenerated. Light, active horses were used for the saddle, and in Rome and Florence they were raced riderless, goaded along the streets by 'suspended balls covered with sharp points from a surcingle passed round the body, in such a way that at every stride they rebound against the sides of the animal and prick him severely'. These horses were called BERBERI, though none was pure Barb.

THE GERMAN HORSES, encompassing those of 'Austria Proper, Hungary and Prussia', included a variety of native breeds, none of which apparently could compete with the English Thoroughbreds or hunters but they could 'live on food which would starve an English horse'.

THE FRENCH HORSES were typified by the powerful NORMAN CHARGER or DESTRIER, and mention was also made of the handsome French DILIGENCE horses, the LIMOUSIN saddle horse, the small, hairy roan from the MEUSE valley, the LINGONE horse of the Marne valley, and the BARROIS pony of the Arne valley.

THE NATIVE RUSSIAN HORSE was small, active and hardy but with not much speed at any pace. There had been a superb Russian cavalry breed of horse but huge numbers of them were lost on the march to Sebastopol. For lighter duties they used the COSSACK ponies ('mere galloways').

NORWEGIAN HORSES were almost all the same colour, midway between cream and dun with black manes, tails and dorsal stripe. Several stallions of the breed were introduced into Wales in the early years of the 19th century and left their peculiar markings there.

THE SWEDISH HORSES were smaller than the Norwegian, and of all colours. Their main role was in harness, driven in carrioles with very long shafts, and they were also put to larger carriages, with which the little creatures could gallop a ten-mile stage within the hour.

THE HORSES OF BRITAIN

British horses were generally defined by their roles rather than by their breeds:

THE ENGLISH THOROUGH-BRED For flat-racing and as a hunter and steeplechaser. Skin thinner and hair more silky than common breeds; veins more apparent.

THE HALF-BRED HUNTER, to carry men weighing 12st (76kg) or more and to get over standing jumps in cramped country – better at high jumps, whereas Thoroughbreds were better at long jumps.

THE IRISH HUNTER, neater head than the English hunter, powerfully built, hardy, excellent high jumper, but often sour tempered.

THE CHARGER AND TROOPER – no particular breed but sufficient size and power to carry a heavy dragoon or lifeguardsman against opposing cavalry, and 'so much handiness at all paces that complete control may be maintained with the bridle-hand, while the sword, lance, or carbine is used by the other'.

THE COVERT, ROAD AND PARK HACK, a type specially intended for the saddle and to be used on some kind of road – a galloper for the covert, a trotter for the turnpike, and a showy trotter for the park.

THE LADIES' HORSE, a perfect park-hack but 'moulded in somewhat longer proportions, so as to give room for the habit to spread without quite eclipsing the animal'.

THE COB, a thick, strongly made hack about 14hh and suited to carry from 15 – 20st (81 – 127kg), the 20-stone cob being in fact a compact and active little cart-horse.

THE GALLOWAY – 'the term itself as well as the animal it represents are quite out of date' but it originally described the full-sized ponies bred in southern Scotland and showing more eastern blood than the Highlanders, seldom exceeding 14 hands.

PONIES, among which there was great variety but the breeds were seldom kept distinct except for the following:

WELSH PONY, often cream, or dun with dark back stripe and dark mane and tail, supposedly from Norwegian sires. 'The Welsh pony is extremely disposed to be obstinate; but as man is very apt to convey his own qualities to the dumb creatures about him, and as obstinacy is notoriously prevalent among the biped inhabitants of the province …'

NEW FOREST PONY, which 'will shortly be as seldom met with as the red deer in that district, that is to say, running wild, for the whole forest is to be broken up into farms'; the breed being 'more useful than ornamental, and not too highly gifted with the former quality either'.

EXMOOR PONY, particularly hardy, with a short, thick middle; 'capital' jumper, capable of carrying a heavy man up and down the Devonshire hills; remarkable for a 'peculiarly light bay colour of the muzzle and legs'. Experiments being made in crossing native mares with Thoroughbreds, trotters and Arabs.

THE HIGHLAND PONY, remarkable for its docility and good manners, ideal shooting pony, 'can be taught almost anything, except perhaps to gallop with the racehorse'. Cat hams like the old Welsh breed. Highly intelligent. Capable of carrying a six-foot Scotsman.

THE SHETLANDER, the smallest variety of the British horse, 9 – 11 hh;

head almost concealed by rough shaggy mane and forelock. Powers 'proportionally as great as that of a dray-horse, and appear to carry with ease a man of 11 or 12 stone, if only he can arrange his legs so as to avoid walking and riding at the same time'.

BRITAIN'S RARE BREEDS TODAY

The Rare Breeds Survival Trust is keeping a watchful eye on the low numbers of several breeds (1986 survey):

BRITISH SPOTTED PONY, CASPIAN, CLEVELAND BAY, CLYDESDALE, DALES PONY, ERISKAY PONY, EXMOOR PONY, SHIRE, SUFFOLK.

In addition, the FELL PONY was listed as endangered in 1983 but its numbers have since increased. The SHIRE is doing better every year too.

ERISKAY PONY

The Eriskay is the most rare of all: it is the last survivor of the original Western Isles or Hebrides pony–a breed with Norse connections and probably Celtic origins (there are comparable animals on Pictish headstones). Most of the old island ponies have disappeared through crossbreeding: those of Skye were improved by the use of Arabians and Highlands; those of Uist by Spanish, Arabian, Norwegian and Clydesdale; those of Barra by stolen Arabians. The Rhum, small and beautiful, ran wild in 1840. And some people still have distant memories of the small, sprightly ponies of Mull.

BREED GROUPS

THE ARABIAN INFLUENCE

The Arab has had a huge influence on horse-breeding: there is Arab blood in many breeds today. As well as the original Arab, there are also national Arabs such as the Egyptian, the Persian, the Syrian and the Turkish Arabs, and the Hungarian Shagya or Babolna Arab and Polish Arab. Several breeds are said to have their faintly Arabian looks as the result of long-ago shipwrecks when Arab horses found themselves in unlikely places, and these include Indian breeds like the KATHIAWARI, the MANIPURI and the MARWARI. Numerous breeds have been influenced by the Arab but, as Abbas Pasha said to Herr Von Hugel (chief of staff to the king of Württemberg in the 19th century): 'Even if you succeed in getting hold of genuine Arabs, you will never have real ones from them, for an Arab horse is no longer an Arab when he ceases to breathe the air of the desert.'

AMERICANS

The 16th century Conquistadores bequeathed their Spanish horses to the newly discovered continent, and many of the 'wild' horses of the Americas are descended from the Spanish animals, many of them Andalusian. Feral and domesticated ones today include:

CRIOLLO breeds of Spanish America
BOLIVIAN and MEXICAN ponies
APPALOOSA
MUSTANG and INDIAN PONY
PINTO
GALICENO of Mexico
PASO FINO of Puerto Rico, Peru and Colombia
PERUVIAN PASO or STEPPING HORSE

The last two breeds are noted for their special gaits, which include very comfortable long-distance styles. Several other American horses have been bred specially for their ability to carry people for long periods in some comfort:

TENNESSEE WALKING HORSE, developed by southern plantation owners from the old

NARRAGANSETT PACER with Arab, Morgan and Thoroughbred blood. The foundation sire was a Standardbred called BLACK ALLAN, foaled 1886, who had a preference for travelling with a half-walk, half-run four-beat gait. There is also the AMERICAN WALKING PONY of Georgia, originally a cross of the Tennessee and the Welsh pony.

MISSOURI FOX TROTTER, a sorrel breed from the Ozark hills, has a strange, broken gait: its forefeet perform a brisk walk while its hind legs trot, and it can be surprisingly comfortable for a rider. Its ancestry includes Morgan, Arab and Thoroughbred.

AMERICAN SADDLE HORSE of Kentucky, developed in the 19th century from Morgan, Thoroughbred, Canadian and the American Trotter; also known as the five-gaited horse because of its characteristic high-stepping action which includes (in the show-ring) a prancing 'slow-gait' and a full-speed 'rack'. Like the Tennessee Walking Horse, the Saddle Horse's dock muscles are nicked when it is young in order to encourage an artificially high tail carriage.

Other American horses bred for speed:

AMERICAN STANDARDBRED or TROTTER, a famous harness racing breed developed in the early 19th century from the Morgan, the Thoroughbred, the Hackney and the Narragansett pacer. Many of the breed can pace as well as trot.

QUARTER HORSE, the most popular breed in America, developed originally in the 18th century colonies of Virginia and the Carolinas, when mares of Andalusian descent were crossed with colonists' English Thoroughbred-type stallions and there evolved a horse which was selectively bred for sprinting in races down a town's main street or along rough tracks cleared through forests and scrub. These sprints covered a quarter of a mile, hence the breed came to be called the Quarter Horse. The type was also ideal for rounding up cattle: it had excellent 'cow sense' and was agile, very fast, intelligent and with exceptionally quick reflexes. (The Canadian equivalent is the Cutting Horse.)

Today the breed's headquarters are in Amarillo, Texas, and the powerfully built, beautifully balanced horse with a kind but lively nature is unbeatable over 2 furlongs.

The first great Thoroughbred progenitor of the Quarter Horses was JANUS, grandson of the Darley Arabian, who was born in England in 1746, raced there and was at stud for two years before coming to Virginia in 1757, where he was bred to mares developed by the Chicasaw and Cherokee Indians from Spanish horses.

Other American breeds or colour types include the ALBINO, CREME and WHITE, the AMERICAN MINIATURE (Shetland), the spotted horses (APPALOOSA, COLORADO RANGER, KANATA PONY, MOROCCO SPOTTED and PONY OF THE AMERICAS), the PALOMINO and PINTO, the MORGAN, the various island ponies

A little Falabella meets a giant Whitbread Brewery shire horse. (Hulton)

(ASSATEAGUE, CHINCOTEAGUE, SABLE ISLAND) and, near Buenos Aires, the tiniest horse in the world – the FALABELLA.

THE TINIES

FALABELLA, less than 7 hh, bred originally by the Falabella family in Argentina from very small Shetlands crossed with small Thoroughbreds, though it is said they were developed over a period of 70 years by inbreeding and crossing a small group of undersized horses discovered in southern Argentina. More of a pet than a horse! A mare only 15 in tall (38 cm) and weighing 26¼ lb (11.9 kg) was bred by Julio Falabella of Recco de Roca before he died in 1981, and a stallion called LITTLE PUMPKIN, foaled April 1973 and owned by J C Williams Jr of Della Terra Mini Horse Farm in South Carolina, was 14 in high (35.5 cm) and weighed 20 lb (9.07 kg) in November 1975.

SHETLAND PONY or SHELTIE, a dwarf at 9 to 10 hh, but very strong and very hardy, with plenty of shaggy mane and tail.

TIMOR, native to the Indonesian island, from 9 to 11 or 12 hh, strong and agile, great endurance.

CASPIAN, the beautifully proportioned miniature horse, 9–11 hh, with a head similar to the Arabian but its home is Iran. Very rare, but bred in Britain since 1972. Had been thought long extinct but a small group of survivors was found in northern Iran in 1965. There is evidence of small, fine horses in the Middle East as far back as 3000 BC and some think they were the ancestors of the hot-blood breeds such as the Arab.

SKYROS, the Greek island pony ridden in bareback races, with a copious mane and tail, very reminiscent of the Parthenon frieze horses, and only 9–11 hh.

PENEIA, another Greek pony from Peloponnese, 10–14 hh. The PINDOS is Greece's only other native pony today and is perhaps 12–13 hh. No doubt both breeds would achieve more size given improved feeding.

GARRANO or MINHO, a Portuguese mountain pony 10–12 hh;

like many other small ponies it has plenty of mane and tail and is very sure-footed and strong. Nearly always a dark chestnut.

MANIPURI, descended from Mongolians and Arabs, is 11–13 hh and is reputed to be the original polo pony.

SPITI, a Himalayan pony bred by the Kanyat tribes and about 12 hh; closely related to the Bhutia and similar to the dun Nanfan of Tibet.

BALI, BATAK, JAVA, SUMBA, TIMOR and SANDALWOOD, Indonesian ponies generally 12–13 hh. The Sandalwood is particularly pretty, and is popular for bareback races.

DARTMOOR, EXMOOR and WELSH MOUNTAIN ponies have height limits of 12.2 hh, like the GOTLAND, an old Scandinavian breed.

Other dwarves include the BHIRUM, the BOLIVIAN CRIOLLO, the CHYANTA and the GUANGXI.

STRANGE BREEDS

BALUCHI, with ears turning inwards (Pakistan).

BASHKIR CURLY, with a long, curly winter coat (Nevada, possibly from Mongolian type).

BUCKSKIN, golden American breed with black dorsal stripe.

HINIS, an Anatolian with short forelegs.

KATHIAWARI, with inturned ears like the Baluchi (Gujarat).

SORRAIA, dun with dark dorsal stripes and with zebra leg markings – typical primitive type and Spain's only native pony (Spanish / Portuguese borders).

VYATKA, usually roan but with black back stripe and shoulder stripe as well as zebra leg markings (Udmurt, USSR).

YAKUT, another with back, shoulder and leg stripes but main body colour can be bay, grey-brown or grey (Siberian).

Painting of Dartmoor ponies looking for food. (ILN)

BODY LANGUAGE

BODIES

BONES

The horse is said to have about 210 individual bones, excluding those of the tail, but in the 1860s Stonehenge, who considered himself something of an anatomist, reckoned there were 247 separate bones!

MOUTH

Equine lips are large, mobile and highly prehensile (i.e. able to grasp) for food-gathering. Unlike cattle, horses have sharp front teeth on the upper jaw as well as the lower, for cropping grass (cattle have an upper pad for tearing rather than cutting grass) which is then ground between broad, strong cheek teeth. There are 40 teeth altogether – 12 incisors, 24 molars and 4 canines or 'tushes' (males only).

A rough idea of the horse's age can be gained from its teeth, especially the incisors, of which there are two complete sets: the temporary, milk or foal teeth, and the permanent or horse teeth. The temporary tooth is small and white with a distinct 'neck' and a short fang, which practically disappears as the tooth gets older because of the pressure from the growing

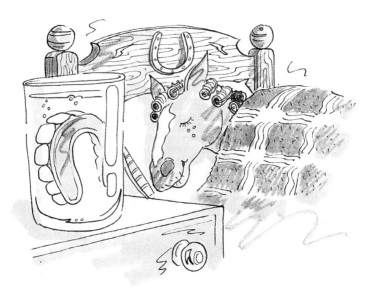

permanent tooth beneath, until its remnant is pushed out of the jaw by the new tooth. The permanent tooth is larger and stronger; it has no marked neck; it has a long, stout fang and is browner in colour. The teeth continue to grow and be worn away throughout the horse's life, and they definitely change in shape and appearance with time, so that they form a good guide to an animal's age.

AGE

The age of a Thoroughbred is calculated from 1st January, regardless of the real date of birth, and of other horses from 1st May. The usual life span is perhaps 20–25 years, though there are many exceptions reaching 40 or even 50 (and the record for an ass is 63).

OLD BILLY, foaled 1760 and believed to be a Cleveland Bay with Eastern blood, was bred by Edward Robinson of Wild Grave Farm in Woolston, Lancashire. He was sold when two or three years old to the Mersey and Irwell Navigation Company and worked the barges for them until 1819, when he was retired to a farm at Latchford, near Warrington. He died there on 27 November 1822, at the remarkable age of 62. His skull is in Manchester Museum, and his stuffed head (fitted with false teeth!) is in Bedford Museum.

TOPOLINO, an ex-Italian army horse foaled in Libya on 24 February 1909, died in Brescia in 1960, aged 61.

A PONY owned by a farmer in central France, foaled 1919, was reliably recorded as reaching the age of 54, a record for ponies.

BONNIE LASS, a roan pony owned by twin sisters Sylvia Moore and Marion Atkinson of Old Harlow, Essex, died at the age of 42 on 2 May 1987.

JOEY, a moorland pony belonging to June and Rose Osborne of the Glebe Equestrian Centre at Wickham Bishop, Essex, died on his 44th birthday.

TANGO DUKE, foaled 1935, was a chestnut gelding owned by Mrs Carmen J Koper of Barongarook, Victoria. He died on 25 January 1978, at the age of 42 – a record for Thoroughbred race-horses.

HEIGHT

The unit of measurement for horses is the HAND, which is 4 in (10.16 cm). The height is measured from the ground to the highest point of the animal's withers. A height of, say, 62 in (157.5 cm) would be 15 hands 2 in and would be represented as 15.2 h, or 15.2 hh (hands high).

HORSEPOWER

The unit known as horsepower is the power needed to lift 33,000 lb a distance of 1 ft in one minute – which in fact is about 1½ times the power that an average horse can exert. After James Watt had invented his steam engine, he needed to quantify its capacity for work and the most dramatic way of doing so was to compare it with the power of the horse. Experiments showed that a horse could work at a constant rate of 22,000 foot-pounds per minute, and the adoption of 33,000 for the unit of horsepower was somewhat arbitrary. It represents 746 watts.

The French, in setting their metric system, scaled down the unit a little so that a Continental *cheval-vapeur* or *force de cheval* is equivalent to the energy needed to raise 75 kg a metre in a second, representing 735.5 watts.

James Watt's invention was expected to put an end to the working horse, but in fact flesh-and-blood horsepower continued to hold its own for at least half a

A horse-powered engine patented in England in 1829.

century. It was not until 1830 that the first passenger line was built for steam trains (from Liverpool to Manchester) with a speed of only 15 mph – 80 years earlier the Duke of Queensberry had achieved better than 19 mph at Newmarket when he hitched four ridden race-horses (TAWNEY, RODERICK RANDOM, CHANCE and LITTLE DAN) to a light four-wheeled carriage and took them at a steady trot on the highway, covering 19 miles in 53 minutes 27 seconds – and indeed making the first 4 miles in only 9 minutes. Squire Osbaldeston's famous 200-mile relay ride also fairly trounced the steam engine with an average speed of over 23 mph.

The long association of man and horse was not willingly betrayed, and they even invented engines that looked like steam engines but were worked by horses on a tread-mill system, and, as a last resort, someone designed a mechanical tramway disguised as a horse-carriage, complete with dummy horse on wheels!

COLOURS

DUN Dun coats vary from yellowish to greyish or brownish, and the skin is pigmented so that the hooves are slate grey. Some have a dark dorsal stripe and dark long hairs (i.e. mane and tail) but others have no dorsal stripe and the long hairs match the coat colour. BLUE DUN is a fairly unusual coat of lead-coloured hairs, with black points.

PALOMINO is very close to dun: the coat is golden, in shades from dark cream to reddish, and the long hairs are characteristically flaxen or silver. The colour of this Golden Horse is named after Juan de Palomino, who had such an animal presented to him by Cortez in Mexico in 1519 – they were known as Ysabella horses at the time, after the Spanish queen who sponsored Christopher Columbus. Some say that her name was given to the yellow horses because she encouraged their breeding, but others used 'isabella' to describe yellowed linen because they claimed that the queen rarely washed! Today isabella is a dun in which there is no skin pigment, so that the hooves are a waxy yellow, and the long hairs are dirty white or light yellow.

CHESTNUT Coat colour in various shades of brown, from 'flat' to reddish brown, golden brown and liver (mahogany). Long hairs are the same as the coat colour or flaxen. White socks or stockings are common. SORREL is a light chestnut.

BAY Probably the most common colour group – the basic coat colour is brown, red-brown, tan or pale brown. Long hairs and often stockings are black, which distinguishes the bays from the chestnuts, but bays can also have white markings on the legs and face. In many countries BROWN is merely the darkest shade of bay, with a tendency to become black towards the feet.

BLACK True black is rare: the colour usually has a rusty tinge to it, especially in winter when the coat can be almost bay.

GREY Greys are generally born black, dark brown or reddish brown and gradually develop an increasing number of white coat hairs as they mature, looking more and more white as they age. Grey coats are therefore a mixture of white and black hairs, sometimes with red, on a black or slate skin.
DAPPLE GREY The white hairs congregate in round spots.
IRON GREY White hairs evenly distributed in a dark coat.
FLECKED Predominantly black, with occasional clusters of white hairs.
STEEL GREY Shining coat with more black hairs than white.
SILVER GREY Shining coat with a great majority of the hairs being white.
CRANE GREY Lustreless coat with white hairs dominant.

FLEA-BITTEN Favourite colour for Arabians – small darker tufts scattered over the lighter background (said to be similar to the appearance of South African horses suffering from tick bites).
WHITE Generally very silvery rather than actually white – more common in very old greys than as a colour for life. The AMERICAN WHITE used to be called ALBINO: they are born white or very pale with a pink rather than black or slate skin, but most have blue eyes rather than the pink eyes of the true albino. Unless the white animals are genetically dominant white heterozygotes, they are known as AMERICAN CREME; there is also a type of Creme which has cinnamon-coloured skin under its cream coat, with the mane a darker cream and with dark eyes.

ROAN Roan is a mixture of different coloured hairs in the coat – white hairs are interspersed with black, red or yellow hairs.
RED ROAN Red, white and yellow mixture
BLUE ROAN Black sprinkled with white
STRAWBERRY ROAN Chestnut sprinkled with white
BLOODY The 'Bloody Shouldered' and 'Bloody Buttocked' Arabs were so named for the sprinkling of red hairs they bore where appropriate.

GRIZZLE Confusingly, this is an old term for a light flesh-colour or roan, though the word is derived from the French for grey.

PIEBALD Large irregular black patches on a white coat.

SKEWBALD Large bay, chestnut or red patches on a white coat.

PINTO or PAINTED Pied colour – either white coat with dark patches ('Tobiano', originally bred by Don Rafael Tobias in Brazil, c. 1846, and the result of a dominant gene) or basically dark coat with white patches ('Overo', the result of a recessive gene).

A leopard spotted type horse – an unusual and startling sight. (Hulton)

ODD-COLOURED Large patches in more than two colours – e.g. black and bay on white.

SPOTTED Sprinkling of spots on a contrasting background. Typical spotted breeds: APPALOOSA (named after the Palouse river in the territory of the Nez-Perce Indians who originally fixed this spotted breed's characteristics using descendants of the 16th-century Spanish Conquistador horses –

recognized coat patterns are snowflake, leopard, frost, marble, spotted blanket, white blanket); PINZGAUER (spotted Austrian draught breed); KNABSTRUP (very old spotted Danish breed similar to the Frederiksborg and with some Palomino blood in its ancestry); LIBYAN LEOPARD (Barbary); COLORADO RANGER (a colour type rather than a breed) and the extinct Welsh BLAGDEN. There are many spotted animals among the South American CRIOLLO horses which have direct links with Arabians and Barbs. Indeed spotted horses and ponies are found all over the world – and many wild creatures have spotted coats for camouflage (which is why spotted horses were popular with American Indians and the old European cavalries).

MARKS

Most of the recognized marks are white, especially on face or legs.

FACES

BLAZE Broad white splash down the face.

SNIP White or flesh-coloured mark between the nostrils.

STAR White mark on forehead, any shape.

STRIPE Narrow white line running down the face – less width than a blaze.

LEGS

Socks and stockings are assumed to be white. Sometimes the white has dark spots and can be called ERMINE.

SOCK White on the fetlock and part of the cannon. A very short sock just above the coronet is a BAND. But, as this verse suggests, socks were not desirable:

'One white sock, buy a horse;
Two white socks, try a horse;
Three white socks, look well about him;
Four white socks, do without him.'

STOCKING More extensive white on the leg, from coronet to knee or hock.

BODY

DORSAL STRIPE, also called LIST, RAY, EEL-STRIPE: dark line running along the length of the back over the spine, most frequently seen in wild horses, duns, mules and donkeys.

SHOULDER STRIPE Dark line across the shoulders, i.e. at right angles to a dorsal stripe.

ZEBRA MARKS Dark horizontal stripes on the back of the foreleg above the knee and across the lower thigh, sometimes called MULE MARKS or DONKEY MARKS. Typically seen on more primitive breeds.

FUNNY FOOD

Horses are herbivores: their main food is grass and grains, especially oats, maize (corn or mealies), barley, rye, wheat or paddy rice, depending on local custom. In some parts of the world peas and beans are the staple diet.

The Bedouins who bred the Kochlani Arab slept beside their mares and stayed with them while they foaled. Foals were weaned at one month from their mother's milk and then put on camel's milk for a hundred days and then gradually on to wheat, barley, pasted dates – and raw meat for high spirit and courage. (Mares were preferred to stallions – they did not neigh on a raid – and young, unbroken mares were caught and tested in a relentless 50-mile ride and then plunged into water. A good mare's immediate reaction to her ordeal was to tuck into a good feed.)

CARNIVOROUS HORSES

The carnivorous Mares of Diomedes were not entirely imaginary. During the siege of Metz, meat was cut into small pieces and wrapped in bran for feeding to the horses, and in Norway horses and other stock traditionally enjoy a soup of boiled fish. Nor is the carnivorous diet necessarily enforced: in 1900 a correspondent sent the following gruesome story to *The Field*:

'I had two tame sheldrakes and a horse out at grass. One morning I found the horse chewing placidly at the head of a sheldrake, which he must have caught, for it was still struggling. I took it from him, and a few hours afterwards gave it to him again in order to photograph him, and he took it and began chewing it again with apparent enjoyment.'

Another correspondent had a gelding which developed the habit of savaging sheep: he killed five in-lamb ewes, and it was suggested that bowel parasites had given him a craving for animal food.

EXPENSIVE HORSES

FARCEUR, a 7-year-old Belgian stallion, was sold to E G Good at Cedar Falls, Iowa, on 16 October 1917, for $47,500.

A WELSH MOUNTAIN PONY was sold to an Australian builder in 1978 for 21,000 guineas (£22,050).

SEATTLE DANCER, a Thoroughbred yearling, was sold to Robert Sangster and Partners at Keeneland, Kentucky, on 23 July 1985, for $13.1 million.

ACCUMULATOR, a pacer, was syndicated by Wall Street Stables to a stud farm in 1984 for $19.2 million.

THE HUMBLE DONKEY

The lowest price ever paid for livestock was at a sale at Kuruman, in South Africa's Cape Province, in 1934, when donkeys were sold for less than 2p each.

POPULATIONS

The world's equine population in 1988 was estimated at about 75 million, whereas just before the Second World War it was about 100 million (compared with 2,000 million humans) and before the First World War about 50 million. Post-war horse populations of the world have been estimated by the United Nation's Food and Agriculture Organization FAO as follows (in thousands):

1948–52	75,800 (av)
1969–71	64,284 (av)
1977	61,755
1979	64,569
1981	66,192

In 1901 there were more than 3 million horses in Britain (2.6 million of them in agriculture or trade); by 1920 there were 2 million (including 1.4 million draught horses), and by 1934 only 1 million. The only official figures more recently are the Ministry of Agriculture's Census Returns for Agricultural Holdings, which in 1983 gave a round figure of 167,000 horses on British farms and market gardens, of which 6,420 were 'for agricultural or horticultural purposes'.

HORSES AT WORK

19th CENTURY CARRIAGE HORSES

Yorkshire and Lincolnshire produced the best carriage horses, and Shropshire was not far behind. They were mostly the result of crossing the old CLEVELAND BAY (nearly extinct by the middle of the 19th century) and Thoroughbred Eastern horses and the buyers sought an extravagant knee-action for cabriolets. About half such horses in London were hired from jobbers such as Mr East and Messrs Wimbush; others were privately owned.

Less perfect animals drew broughams rather than cabriolets, and particularly plain but heavier types known as heavy machiners drew well sprung omnibuses and

vans at 6 mph (the bigger dray-horses could only manage half that speed at the most). Indeed some pair-drawn omnibuses, laden with 26 passengers, a coachman and a conductor, could travel as fast as 8 miles within the hour.

In England, the trotting horse that rivalled the Americans was the celebrated NORFOLK TROTTER, infused with Eastern blood for endurance. Norfolk had long been famous for its trotting horses and they were much in demand for drawing gigs and phaetons. Their action was more showy than that of American trotters: style was considered more important than speed, 'no purchaser caring for a faster pace than 14 or 15 miles an hour, and most contenting themselves with 12', whereas in

America the stopwatch ruled over the eye.

The Norfolk Trotter, or Norfolk Roadster, evolved some time around 1729 from an Arabian stallion and a Yorkshire Hackney. The HACKNEY was the most stylish trotter imaginable, with a dramatic and beautiful high-stepping style which somehow mirrored the revolution of the wheels: its whole shape and stance are almost unique.

THE CONVEYANCES

The 19th century was the carriage age, especially 1800–40 when Hyde Park was a showplace for carriages, horses and society drivers.

APRIL, 1809: MEETING OF THE FOUR-IN-HAND CLUB:
'The Hon. Lincoln Stanhope appeared with Lord Hawke, and others, in yellow bodied carriages with whips, springs, and dickey-boxes; cattle of a bright bay colour, with plain ornaments on the harness, and rosettes to the ears.' The drivers wore light drab-colour cloth coats, long skirted, with three tiers of pockets, and waistcoats with blue and yellow stripes: fashionable clothes formed an important part of the whole ensemble. Another gentleman wore a *'box driving coat of white drab cloth, with fifteen capes, two tiers of pockets, and an inside one for the Belcher handkerchief; cravat of white muslin, spotted with black. Bouquets of myrtle, pink and yellow geraniums were worn.'*

CONVEYANCES LISTED IN ROGET'S THESAURUS, 1911

Carriage; wagon/waggon, wain, dray, cart, lorry, carriole; truck, tram; limber, tumbrel, pontoon; conestoga-wagon; brett, dearborn, dump-cart, hack, hackery, jigger, kittereen, mail stage, manumotor, rig, rockaway, prairie schooner; sway, sloven, team, tonga; equipage, turn-out; coach, chariot, phaeton, break, wagonette, drag, curricle,

tilbury, whisky, landau, barouche, victoria, brougham, clarence, calash, caleche, britzka, araba, kibitka; berlin; sulky, desobligeant, sociable, vis-a-vis, dormeuse; jaunting car, outside car; dandi, dool, doolie; muchil, palki; runabout; tonjon; vettura; post chaise; diligence, stage; stage-coach, mail-coach, hackney-coach, glass-coach; stage wagon; car, omnibus, fly, cabriolet, cab, hansom, shofle, four-wheeler, growler, droshki, drosky; dogcart, trap, whitechapel, buggy, four-in-hand, unicorn, random, tandem; shandredhan, char-a-bancs; by the Marrowbone Stage.

But the splendid crimson mail-coaches had a very short though romantic history. They were paraded on the king's birthday in all the glory of new paint, the guards in new scarlet coats and gold-laced beaver hats, the horse resplendent in silver-plated harness and coloured rosettes. The procession was always led by the Bristol Mail and made its way to St James's Palace to salute the Royal Family. The last such ceremony was in 1838, and the first had only taken place 36 years earlier. The magnificent and exciting stage coaches were gradually pushed off the kingdom's roads by the coming of the railways.

DRAUGHT HORSES

In Roman times, big European horses and oxen drew the larger goods wagons while lesser horses, mules and donkeys drew lighter carts and two-wheeled passenger vehicles or acted as pack animals. In some places, such as the Netherlands, flat-bottomed barges were drawn by either human or horse power, and in later times British canal barges often relied on sturdy, powerful, steady barge horses too.

In medieval Britain, horses served many purposes and in the 16th century heavy horses hauled people

Engraving of Suffolk mare and her foal. (Hulton)

who did not ride, and they continued to pull poorer classes in stage wagons until displaced by the railways. It was not until the mid-1700s that a light iron swing plough was invented for working horses, rather than the traditional ploughing oxen, but thereafter the agricultural revolution depended on horsepower.

The 18th century was also a period when there were pulling trials or drawing matches for the big horses of Suffolk. Wagons laden with heavy sand and with their wheels sunk into the ground and chocked by wooden blocks were the challenge for the horses, and enormous bets were made on the outcome of their efforts. Pulling contests are still popular today in several countries.

Heavy horses still find work today, especially in the forests, and there are still ploughing competitions but in fact the great age of the horse as the main locomotive power on the farm only lasted about a hundred and fifty years.

THE RISE, FALL AND RISE OF THE HEAVY HORSE

19th century The iron horse began to make its presence felt but the heavy horse found its true role for the short haul, getting the freight to the railhead and also delivering it to its final destination; it remained vital to industry and commerce for goods transport.

1883 Great Western Railway acquired its own horses for the first time (it had used contractors before then): 501 bought for Paddington and Smithfield.

1890s Peak of the heavy horse age. Most London horses were leased by contractors to local councils, fire brigades, tram companies, coal merchants and countless trades and businesses. In 1896 one contractor (Tillings) owned 3,386 horses.

1930s Situation for heavy horses only modestly healthy at the outbreak of the Second World War. During the war effort, tractors were regarded as merely supplementary to working horses, but post-war tractors and motor lorries soon began to oust them.

1963 Heavy horse breeds at all-time low and only just survived.

1966 London Harness Horse Parade instituted. Twenty years later 500 horses took part.

1980s Situation improving. Shire Horse Society initiated a joint project to encourage pragmatic approach to the future of the heavy horses and to give them a proper working role again. Investigations into economic potential for working horses. The optimistic SHS report *History with a Future* was published in 1988 and, as the report so aptly puts it:

'Whereas the Thoroughbred is a symbol of wealth, the heavy horse is a token of the life and work of ordinary people. Thence is derived the almost universal affection in which it is held – even by those who, for a variety of reasons, are prejudiced against the rest of the horse world. It is a reminder of grandad.'

HORSEHAIR

When working horses were abundant, many uses were found for horsehair. For example:

Hair sieves (tamise, or tammy cloth).
Bows for stringed instruments.
Hair mats for draining cider.
Curled-hair filling for mattresses, saddles and seating.
Binding material mixed with wall plaster.
Horsehair cloth and haircord.
Binding for archery bow-notches and arrow feathers.
Crossbow sights (beads threaded on horsehairs).
Gin traps to capture small birds.
Ropes and fishing lines.

HEAVY BREEDS

In Britain today there are really only four breeds of heavy horse: the Shire, the Suffolk, the Clydesdale and the Percheron. There used to be a VARDY HORSE in north-east England, which was an ideal farm horse from a blend of the BAKEWELL BLAKE (a Shire type) and the CLEVELAND BAY, but it became extinct towards the end of the 19th century when the Shire and Clydesdale grew in popularity. Britain is not as rich in old breeds as some other parts of Europe.

BREEDS DESCRIBED BY STONEHENGE (1862)

OLD ENGLISH BLACK CART-HORSE *'From time immemorial this country has possessed a heavy and comparatively misshapen animal, the more active of which were formerly used as chargers or pack-horses, while the others were devoted to the plough, and, as time wore on, to the lumbering vehicles of the period of Queen Elizabeth and her immediate successors. In colour almost invariably black, with a great fiddle-case in the place of head, and feet concealed in long masses of hair, depending from misshapen legs, he united flat sides, upright shoulders, mean and narrow hips, and very drooping quarters. Still, plain as he was, he did his work willingly, and would pull at a dead weight till he dropped.'*

SUFFOLK CART-HORSE The farmers of Norfolk and Suffolk during the 18th century were generally much more advanced than those in other parts of the country, and that included their breeding of cart horses. According to Arthur Young, the best Suffolk horses of those days could pull a five-ton load for 30 miles on secondary sandy roads without tiring, but 'an uglier horse cannot be viewed – it can trot no better than a cow'. What need had a hefty draught horse for fine trotting? Indeed, when Lincolnshire and Yorkshire trotters were used in the 18th and 19th centuries to improve the old Suffolks, John Lawrence remarked:

'I am not aware of the great use of trotting to plough and cart horses.'

The Suffolks of the early 19th

century were described thus:

'Their merit probably consists more in constitutional hardiness than fine shape, being in general a very plain horse. Their colour is mostly yellowish, or sorrel, with a white ratch or blaze on their faces.'

They were deep barrelled, and full in the flank so that they could 'carry their food long, and consequently are able to stand a longer and harder day's work'.

However, that type was quite extinct by the middle of the last century and the improved Suffolk was lighter and quicker, with very clean legs. (Many cart-horse breeds have, or had, heavily feathered legs, which look good but which are less than a blessing to a horse working in muddy conditions or where burrs are abundant.)

THE IMPROVED LINCOLNSHIRE DRAY-HORSE

The Lincolnshire horse was developed at about the same time as the Suffolk, partly for use on Lincoln's heavy clays but chiefly for drawing London drays. The horse was a 'large and magnificently shaped animal, generally known as the Dray-Horse. Many of these stand from seventeen to eighteen hands high, with bodies of enormous girth, and legs, if not in porportion, yet of greater size than in other breeds.' They were the produce of a cross between the Flemish and the old English Black, the latter having 'increased in size and substance, from the nature of the grasses of the district, which seem peculiarly adapted to develop the growth of this animal'. But the Lincolnshire had its drawbacks: 'Unfortunately, both sire and dam are slow, and the produce, from its increased bulk, is rendered still slower, being wholly unfit for agricultural operations in competition with the Suffolk or Clydesdale horses, and only well adapted to move heavy brewers' drays, which cannot from their weight be expected to travel very rapidly.'

CLYDESDALE

Stonehenge describes the Clydesdale as intermediate in size between the Suffolk and the Lincolnshire Dray and says he 'is supposed to be bred from a cross of the Dutch or Flemish horse, imported by the Duke of Hamilton' in the latter part of the 18th century, 'with the active descendants of the pack-horses, which were retained in use longer in the north than in the south'. Prince Albert had one of these horses, which he purchased for £500. The breed had a characteristically long stride and they were universally employed in Scotland, where they generally had their tails docked.

CLEVELAND

'The Cleveland, if it ever existed as a variety of the cart-horse, cannot now be found . . . It is true that he is sometimes used for agricultural purposes, resembling the Suffolk horse in quickness, yet not being equal to him in constitution. But he is chiefly sought after for the carriages of the aristocracy, to which his rich bay colour, and clean legs, often of a jet black, are well suited.'

THE VERMONT CART-HORSE

There was a distinct 19th century breed of draught-horse in the American state of Vermont identical to the Cleveland Bay.

'Although they are emphatically draught-horses, they have none of that shagginess of mane, tail, and fetlocks which indicates a descent from the black horse of Lincolnshire, and none of that peculiar curliness or waviness which marks the existence of Canadian or Norman blood.'

Vermont was also the home of the Justin Morgan.

CONESTOGA DRAUGHT-HORSE

This Pennsylvanian breed was a very large, muscular horse often more than 17 hh and very similar to the heaviest of the German and Flemish cart-horses. As Stonehenge pointed out, most of the early

Shire horses still work daily, making deliveries for the breweries.

settlers in that part of the United States were Germans and would naturally have brought over their own horses or have selected local horses which most resembled the type they remembered from the old country. The Conestoga horses (named for the valley in which it was produced) were 'good honest workers' and were chiefly used for drawing wagons or, when of inferior shape, for canal traffic.

THE FLEMISH HORSE Flemish horses had long had a fine reputation which Stonehenge ascribed to the fact that the Netherlands had 'extensive meadows which are not flooded, and in which the fine clovers, so requisite to the development of the horse, are produced in tolerable abundance'. Their worst point was in their feet: the soles were almost always flat and thin, making them unfit for fast work on hard roads. Yet they were 'extraordinarily good-tempered', and teams of mares were capable of drawing heavy diligences more than 10 miles within the hour in the 1830s.

HANOVERIAN Queen Victoria had a fine team of black carriage-horses of the Hanoverian breed, which were also 'brought over to this country for the use of the undertaker' – though they were more expensive than the Flemish and Holstein horses and were therefore

Norman mares were crossed with English Thoroughbreds to produce horses 'indeed in every way calculated for troop-horses, and should our cavalry ever come in contact with them, and any advantage is to be gained, it must be through superior horsemanship alone'.

BRITISH HEAVY HORSES TODAY

SHIRE A Great Horse descendant, originally called the English Cart-horse: very strong indeed and *very* big and long-legged, but as gentle as they come. A heavy and powerful town and show horse. The tallest in the world: stallions average 17.2 hh, which is too big for good workers. Show horses have four white feet, but black feet are good and hard for work. The Shire Horse Society, founded in 1878, has successfully increased the breed's popularity again and is now leading a general heavy-horse revival. The National Shire Show is at Peterborough. Recognized colours are black, brown, bay or grey; used to register chestnut, piebald and roan (the latter has Clydesdale connections). About thirty Shires work daily in central London making deliveries for Whitbread Breweries; others work for city corporations in Manchester, Leeds and Birmingham.

CLYDESDALE The Lanarkshire heavy horse with Flemish blood is sometimes called the Shire with a Scottish accent but is more active than the Shire, and there is definite geographical preference – Shires in the south, Clydesdales in the north. Usually brown or bay with lots of white on face and on well-feathered legs. Used to be popular with railway contractors, city corporations, tram companies (Glasgow bought 4,000 Clydesdales for trams in one year at its peak). Even in 1927 it was more

'only used by the most fashionable houses of that trade'. They were remarkable for the length and beauty of their manes and tails, and for their brilliant black coats.

NORMAN CHARGER or DESTRIER This massive but elegant horse had been celebrated for a long time as the type of horse which combined show and utility. The French horses had legs and feet 'so sound that they are able to trot over the paved roads at a pace which, slow as it is, would speedily lame our English horses of similar size and strength' and they were so good-tempered that stallions and mares could be used together in all kinds of work. The lightest, stoutest

A Percheron stallion. (Keystone)

economical than petrol-driven vehicles for haulage up to two miles and several city authorities still employ a few Clydesdales today. The borough of Douglas has had a unique horse-drawn tram system since 1876; it used 53 horses in 1987, mostly Clydesdale × Hunter.

SUFFOLK (PUNCH) The old 'Sorrel Horse' seen in pub signs. Clean-legged, and always chestnut (in seven recognized shades from nearly brown to a pale mealy). Still worked in steep areas of the West Country, where four legs are safer than four wheels, and it has the soundest foot of any breed. The most ancient of our heavy breeds in purity of blood and therefore in consistency of appearance over several centuries, though the modern Suffolk can be traced back to a horse foaled in 1760. Ideal for agriculture as opposed to road and town work, though Aberdeen City Council uses Suffolks as well as Clydesdales. Society formed 1877.

PERCHERON A solid black or grey French horse but its type came to Britain at the time of the Norman conquest and was continuously imported in the 13th and 14th centuries. Exceptionally hardy, even on poor feeding; able to work in atrociously muddy conditions, where its clean legs are a great advantage. Extensively used as a cross on Shire mares for working horses; excellent temperament for city work. Percherons are used by the jam-makers, Chivers. Annual show at Midsummer Common, Cambridge.

RECORD-BREAKERS

LARGEST HORSE EVER RECORDED

BROOKLYN SUPREME was a purebred red roan Belgian Brabant standing 19.2 hh at the withers. Foaled 1928, died 1948. Owned by C G Good at Ogden, Iowa. The horse weighed 1.44 tonnes at its maximum in 1938 and had a chest girth of 102 in (259 cm). His feet were big too: each shoe weighed 7½ lb (3.4 kg) and measured 14 in (35.5 cm) across.

WILMA DU BOS, foaled 15 July 1966, was a Belgian Brabant. When she was shipped to a new owner, she was heavily in foal and weighed 3,218 lb (1,469 kg), standing 18.2 hh, and with a maximum girth of 12 ft (3.65 m). Arriving in New York, she scaled 3,084 lb (1,399 kg), but after foaling she reverted to her normal weight of about 2,500 lb (1,088 – 1,134 kg).

TALLEST HORSES

SAMPSON (later named MAMMOTH) was the tallest horse on record. A Shire, bred by Thomas Cleaver of Toddington Mills, Bedfordshire, and foaled in 1846, he measured 21.2½ hands in 1850 and later weighed 30 cwt (1,524 kg).

WANDLE GOLIATH, foaled 1977 and owned by Young & Company's Brewery in Wandsworth, and EXTRA STOUT, foaled 1980 and owned by Samuel Smith's Brewery at Tadcaster, Yorkshire, are Britain's tallest living horses. Both are Shires and both measure 19.1½ hands.

STRONGEST

VULCAN, a Shire gelding owned by Liverpool Corporation, pulled the equivalent to a starting load of 29 tons on a dynamometer at the British Empire Exhibition at Wembley on 23 April 1924, and on the same occasion a pair of Shires easily pulled a starting load of 50 tons, the maximum which the

Extra Stout, one of Britain's tallest living horses, with two small friends. (Samuel Smith Brewery)

dynamometer could register.

TWO SHIRES hauled the greatest load ever by a pair of draught-horses in February, 1893, near Ewer, Michigan, when they allegedly pulled a loaded sledge litter weighing 144 short tons (130.9 tonnes) for 400 yds (365.8 m) along a frozen road at the Nester Estate. In fact the claim was exaggerated: the load of 50 logs of white pine actually weighed about 53 short tons (42.3 tonnes). The horses themselves had a combined weight of 3,500 lb (1,587 kg).

BIG TEAMS

Samuel Smith's Brewery at Tadcaster brought out a unique team of 12 grey Shires at the end of 1987. Each weighs about a ton and their heights range from 17 to 19.1½ hands. EXTRA STOUT is the offside wheeler.

In Australia the biggest yoke ever harnessed was 76 draught horses, strung out in pairs, to pull a 14-ton wool wagon out of a river in full flood. Many of the horses were Clydesdales. Elsewhere there have been teams of 16 Clydesdales yoked to multi-furrow ploughs.

HEAVIES

HONEST TOM, foaled 1884, holds the British weight record. He was 17.2 hh and scaled 2,912 lb (1,325 kg) in 1891. His owner was James Forshaw of Littleport, Cambridgeshire.

PINCHBECK UNION CREST, foaled 1964, is a champion Percheron stallion and the heaviest

horse living in Britain today, with a peak weight fluctuating between 2,520 – 2,632 lbs (1,143 – 1,194 kg). His father SALTMARSH SILVER CREST (1955 – 78) weighed 2,772 lbs (1,257 kg) at his heaviest.

HIGHEST PRICE

FARCEUR, a seven-year-old Belgian stallion, was bought by EGGood at Cedar Falls, Iowa, on 16 October 1917, for a record draught-horse price of $47,500.

THE WORLD'S WORK HORSES

ARDENNAIS/AUXOIS
BOULONNAIS/BRABANT
BRETON
COMTOIS
DUTCH DRAUGHT
FJORD/FLEMISH
FRANCHES-MONTAGNES or
    FREIBERG
FRIESIAN
HUNGARIAN DRAUGHT
IRISH DRAUGHT
ITALIAN HEAVY DRAUGHT
JUTLAND/LATVIAN
LITHUANIAN HEAVY
    DRAUGHT
MURAKOZ/NORIKER
NORTH SWEDISH
PERCHERON/POITEVIN
RHINELAND or RHENISH
RUSSIAN
SCHLESWIG
SOKOLSKY
SOVIET
TRAIT DU NORD
VLADIMIR

ON THE RUN

OVER THE STICKS

As hunting in Britain became increasingly impeded by the land enclosures of the 17th and 18th centuries, people began to enjoy rather than resent the barriers of hedges, ditches and wooden rails: they were a challenge to the rider. As well as chasing foxes and other prey across the new landscape, they raced each other from one landmark to another purely for the thrill of competition and generally under the incentive of substantial wagers. Church steeples were suitably prominent landmarks for such races.

Thus hunting was the basis for the sport of jumping over farmland boundaries which in due course became amateur point-to-pointing on the one hand and organized, professional jump-racing on regular public courses on the other.

Gradually the needs of the spectators were taken into consideration; the local farmers who had allowed hunting over their land during the season were given very good lunches in marquees put up near the finishing point and eventually the course became a circuit so that both start and finish could be seen by most of the spectators. Then urban spectators began to enjoy the sport and the hunt committees had to take a more professional attitude in order to cater for them. The end-of-season 'jolly' became a money-making race meeting, with income raised by car-parking charges, and with carefully maintained brush fences rather than a general free-for-all over the local hedges.

SOME STEEPLECHASING DATES

1752 To settle a wager, Cornelius O'Callaghan and Edmund Blake raced four and a half miles across country from the Church of St Buttevant in County Cork, Ireland, to the spire of St Leger, to prove which had the better horse. Blake was the winner.

1792 Eight-mile steeplechase from Barkby Holt to Coplow and back: the favourite's rider took a hundred-yard shortcut through a friend's back garden and the horse that came second was 'rather fat'.

1803 First 'regular' steeplechase in Ireland, inspired by a hunt dinner.

1830 First annual jumping meeting, the St Albans Steeplechase, organized by the proprietor of the Turf Hotel; 16 starters.

1833 First Cheltenham meeting.

1836 First Liverpool meeting. Opening event won by Capt. Becher.

1837 First forerunner of the Grand National run at Maghull.

1839 First race at Aintree, called the Grand Liverpool Steeplechase, won by LOTTERY ridden by the professional Jem Mason. 4-mile course, mostly over plough, 29 obstacles including the Brook where Captain Becher came to grief riding

The first regular steeplechase was held in Ireland in 1803. (Fotomas)

CONRAD. Winner's time: 14 minutes 53 seconds.

1847 Aintree race first called the Grand National.

THE GRAND NATIONAL

4½ miles with 30 jumps.
Highest jump The Chair – 5 ft 2 in (1 m 55 cm) high × 3 ft 9 in (92.2 cm) thick.

THE GREAT GRAND NATIONAL HORSES

ABD-EL-KADER The first double winner (1850, 1851). Stood at 15 hh. His dam had pulled the Salisbury coach.

BATTLESHIP No bigger than a polo pony, the second American-bred winner in 1938, ridden by Bruce Hobbs at the age of 17, the youngest jockey ever to win. Battleship was sired by the famous MAN O'WAR.

THE COLONEL Double winner (1869, 1870), with Exmoor pony blood on sire's side. His jockey,

George Stevens, had a record 5 wins in the National.

CONRAD Captain Becher's mount when he fell at the Brook which was subsequently named after him.

DEVON LOCH The Queen Mother's horse, loudly cheered by a loyal 1956 crowd as he led from the last ditch, looking quite unbeatable 50 yards from the finish when suddenly his hind legs went from under him and he skidded spreadeagled on his stomach, legs outstretched. With Dick Francis still in the saddle, the horse managed to gain his feet but seemed to be unable to use his hindlegs. E.S.B. sailed by and took the race. Devon Loch was unsaddled where he stood and, miraculously, walked away absolutely sound after a minute or two. Veterinary inspection could find nothing wrong with him at all: he was neither exhausted nor hard-ridden.

JAY TRUMP Winner in 1965 and the first horse to take the National and the Maryland Hunt Cup. Ridden in both by owner and

leading American amateur, Tommy Crompton Smith.

THE LAMB Double winner (1868 and 1871). His owner foresaw the second win in a dream – just like most hopeful owners!

L'ESCARGOT Beat Red Rum in 1975 and had Gold Cup victories in 1970 and 1971. Owned by the American, Raymond Guest.

LOTTERY First winner of the National in 1839. The 16 hh bay was still winning races at the age of 16, and then retired to become a plough horse.

LUTTEUR III Won for France in

Lottery, first winner of the National in 1839. (ILN)

1909 as a five-year-old. Ridden by Georges Parfrement using leathers far shorter than was the fashion of the time. Thereafter the style for long leathers over the sticks changed. (Jockeys in flat-racing had begun to adopt the American-style short leathers from about 1900.)

MANIFESTO An all-time great, winner in 1897 and 1899, almost won in 1900. Ran a record eight times between 1895 and 1904, with a total of two wins and four places.

and swam ashore. He was sold after his Grand National win to King Edward VII and ran for him in the 1905 National. In 1911 he was ridden by Lord Kitchener in the coronation procession of King George V.

RED RUM The greatest triple winner of them all. Sprint-bred, he raced as a two-year-old. His trainer, taxi-driver 'Ginger' McCain, was as famous as the horse. He and his passenger, Noel Le Mare, bought

THE GRAND NATIONAL 1977

R E D R U M

Some horses come, some horses go, whose names will last for years.
And one of these is with us now whose feat brought floods of tears.
Three times he won round Aintree and his spirit did not fade.
He was sublime and gentle and a touch of class displayed.
So let us not forget this horse, stand up and beat the drum.
When tales of Aintree shall be told the answer is RED RUM.

A tribute to Red Rum on the wall of the winner's enclosure at Aintree Race Course.
(Hulton)

MERRYMAN II Winner in 1960. Bought as a hunter for £200 by Miss Winifred Wallace of Edinburgh, who won three point-to-points with the horse. Third winner trained by Neville Crump, and first clear favourite to win in 33 years. Only one ever to win the treble of Foxhunters' Chase, Grand National and Scottish Grand National.

MOIFAA 1904 winner at 25 to 1, from New Zealand. 17 hh brown gelding which 'looked like a starved elephant'. Bought for £500 by Mr Spencer Gollan, a wealthy New Zealand sheep farmer and bloodstock breeder who raced in England and who was run over by a London bus in 1934. The horse was shipwrecked on his way to England,

Red Rum in 1972 as a seven-year-old, unaware that the bay gelding had been treated for a form of arthritis. Winner in 1973, 1974, 1977, and runner-up in 1975 and 1976. Set all-time record of 9 minutes 1.9 seconds in 1973, carrying 10st 5lb (65.8kg) and ridden by Brian Fletcher (average 29.8mph). Was 12 years old and carrying top weight of 11st 8lb (73.5kg) when he won by 25 lengths in 1977. Withdrawn because of injury within 24 hours of the start of the 1978 National and was paraded there in a tearful farewell.

ROQUEFORT Once drew a dog-cart but won in 1885.

ROYAL TAN Gallant old horse finished 1st (1954), 2nd and 12th.

One of the trio of winners trained by O'Brien (others were EARLY MIST, 1953 winner, and QUARE TIMES, 1955).

RUBIO First American-bred winner (1908). Foaled in California, sold as two-year-old for 15 guineas at Newmarket and broke down so badly that he was demoted to pulling a hotel bus meeting trains at Towcester until he was fit for training.

CHELTENHAM

First Gold Cup 1924, first Champion Hurdle 1927. Gold Cup course is now 3¼ miles, Hurdle 2 miles.

Fastest Gold Cup 6 min 23.4 sec (SILVER FAME, 1951).

Fastest Champion Hurdle 3 min 51.7 sec (SEE YOU THEN, 1985)

CHELTENHAM CHAMPIONS

ARKLE was the greatest Cheltenham winner of all, taking the Gold Cup three times in succession (1964–6) ridden by Pat Taaffe. Foaled in 1957 in Ireland, he was a big bay gelding, fast and fluid over the jumps. He seemed to have the 'extra leg' to get out of trouble and was a superb sprinter on the stretch. Arkle won several of his races carrying 35 lb (15.9 kg) more than any rival. He dominated the British steeplechasing scene until a small fracture ended his career after his 35th race in December 1966.

DESERT ORCHID, fondly known as Dessie, is the outstanding British steeplechaser of the 1980s. Foaled in 1979, the grey overcame an idiosyncratic preference for right-hand courses and an aversion to heavy going when he took the Cheltenham Gold Cup in 1989 under atrocious conditions – snow on the slopes and torrential rain. It was the 27th win of his career (out of 54 starts – including 9 2nds and 5 3rds) and, ridden by Simon

Sherwood, he overtook Yahoo 75 yards from the winning post. Owned by Richard Burridge, trained by David Elsworth. Jump debut in January 1983 at Kempton, first win (at Ascot) in October 1983 by 20 lengths. In February 1989 efforts to have the Hampshire horse created a freeman of the Surrey borough of Elmbridge, in recognition of his ability to draw crowds to Sandown Park and business to the borough, failed because the horse was 'not, legally speaking, a person': the freedom could only be conferred on 'persons of distinction'.

GOLDEN MILLER Winner in 1934 Grand National and also won five consecutive Cheltenham Gold Cups (1932–6).

THE PARDUBICKA

The Pardubicka is Prague's answer to the Grand National, with its own long, daunting and inspiring history. A hundred years ago cavalry officers of the Central Powers regiments raced against gentlemen and professional jockeys whose horses had been bred by princes. The course is 4 miles 556 yards with 30 different fences (at Aintree there are 16 different fences, 14 of which are taken twice). The course was built in 1874 by the Bohemian Racing Association, which created an Irish Bank 6 ft 6 in high (2 m) and the same in width, and the terrifying Taxis fence 4 ft 11 in (1.5 m) in both dimensions but with a ditch 16 ft 6 in (5 m) across.

The first winner of the Pardubicka was ridden by a British professional jockey, when the stewards were a count and two princes, the starter also a count and the judge a princely field marshal. Before the First World War, British jockeys won the event twenty times but only one of them (George Williamson, 1890) also won our own Grand National (Manifesto, 1899), and only one native

Pardubicka regular won at Aintree (Count Karel Kinsky).

In 1927 a Count Kinsky niece, Lata Brandisova, was entered as a rider in the Pardubicka, and the shocked Bohemian aristocrats asked our Jockey Club for a ruling on women. 'Let the gel ride!' was the verdict, and 'the gel' certainly did: she was placed three times and finally won the race in 1937. In 1947, after twenty years with the Pardubicka, she fell badly and her career was over.

In 1973 Chris Collins, well known English point-to-pointer and perfumer (Goya), was the first Englishman to enter the Pardubicka for over fifty years–*and* he won it in record time on the favourite STEPHEN'S SOCIETY.

ON THE FLAT

The first recorded race in Britain was in AD 210 at Netherby in Cumbria between horses imported by the Roman Emperor Lucius Septimus Severus. The first regular meeting was at Smithfield in London in 1174, when there were weekly horse fairs on Fridays. The first prize on record was a purse of gold presented by Richard the Lionheart in 1195 for a 3-mile race. The first official blessing for English racing was given by Chester city council in 1511 when it permitted the holding of annual races. It was a sport for the aristocracy, and for honour and glory rather than gain, and it was a very English sport until the 19th century. It also gave birth to one of the most famous breeds of all time: the Thoroughbred.

HISTORY OF THE THOROUGHBRED

HENRY VIII In order to breed better horses for war, an act was passed forbidding the turning out of any entire horse older than two years and less than 15 hh on

commons in 25 English counties and Wales. Elsewhere, for some reason, the lower height limit was 14 hh. Small, weedy mares and foals had to be destroyed.

QUEEN ELIZABETH I Henry VIII's laws apparently did not produce what was wanted. By the time of the Spanish Armada, only 3,000 suitable English horses could be gathered for the cavalry, and only with serious interruption to the main form of internal transport, by packhorse. But on the Spanish ships there were plenty of beautiful Andalusians, then considered the best horses in Europe, and these were possessed by the victorious admiral and presented to the Queen in order to improve the English breed. Spanish horses continued to be imported for at least a century.

STUARTS First time that horse-breeding was taken seriously in England–many Arabian animals imported.

JAMES I First clear account of an imported Eastern horse: the London merchant, Mr Markham, brought in an Arabian from Constantinople and sold it to the King for the then enormous sum of £500. The MARKHAM ARABIAN proved too slow to race but was put to stud.

17TH CENTURY By the mid 17th century racing was well established in England, though the meetings were few and small, but when light cavalry replaced heavy armour because of the advent of gunpowder, racing became much more popular. Large, strong, spirited Neapolitan horses and plenty of Arabs, Barbs and Turks were introduced to breed turf and saddle horses.

The influence of these elegant foreign horses quickly reformed the old heavy chargers which had been able to carry knights in full armour weighing on average 20–25 stone (127–158 kg).

CROMWELL Oliver Cromwell's stud groom, Mr Place, obtained

PLACE'S WHITE TURK; little is known about the horse but he was extensively used for breeding.

CHARLES II The King imported four Barb mares, known as the ROYAL MARES, from Tangiers, and they were crossed to Fairfax's MOROCCO BARB and the Duke of Buckingham's HELMSLY TURK. In 1684 three Hamburg mares, known as the THREE TURKS, were taken at the siege of Vienna.

In the 19th century Stonehenge was of the opinion that 'the use of the Spanish, mixed, perhaps, with native English blood in the mare, was the real cause of the success which attended the cross with the Barb; the mare being of greater size and stride than the horse, and giving those qualities to the produce, while the horse brought out the original strain of Eastern blood, which possessed the wind and endurance so peculiar to it'. He concluded that the English Thoroughbred was based on these imported horses and included:

NATIVE MARES used for racing, and bred from Spanish and English strains (the former probably descended from the Barbs of Morocco).

MARKHAM'S ARABIAN, though he 'proved to be good for nothing, and most probably there is now not the slightest strain of his blood extant'.

PLACE'S WHITE TURK, to whom 'most of our best horses can be traced, through MATCHEM'.

THE THREE TURKS from the siege of Vienna.

THE ROYAL MARES imported by Charles II from the Levant.

Various other horses and mares were mentioned in early pedigrees between the times of Charles II and James II and from then on the repeated use of Arabian, Turk and Barb blood proved excellent for the English racehorse. The real golden era of the exotic sires came after the reign of James II and the three great foundation sires of the modern Thoroughbred were the Darley Arabian, the Godolphin Arabian and the Byerly Turk:

THE BYERLY TURK, foundation sire of the HEROD line and ancestor of DIOMED (first winner of the Epsom Derby), served during the Irish Wars as Captain Byerly's charger in about 1689 and was thereafter put to stud.

THE DARLEY ARABIAN is credited as the foundation sire of the ECLIPSE line. He was imported some time between 1700 and 1715 (probably 1704), and belonged to Mr Darley of Buttercramb, near York, who bought the horse through his brother, a merchant at Aleppo (Syria). Tradition says that the horse was a native of Palmyra.

THE GODOLPHIN ARABIAN, also known as the BERBER GODOLPHIN, is the sire of the MATCHEM line. He was a very rich brown-bay, about 15 hh, and was originally sent to France by the Emperor of Morocco as a gift to Louis XIV, but the horse's worth was not appreciated and he was reduced to drawing a water-cart in the streets of Paris, whence he was rescued in about 1730 by Edward Coke. Even Coke failed to recognize his potential, however, and only used him as a teaser for HOBGOBLIN. The Godolphin's moment of glory came when Hobgoblin refused to cover the mare ROXANA, and so the 'teaser' obliged instead. The result of the mating was LATH, the most celebrated racehorse of his day. The Godolphin then quickly got CADE (sire of MATCHEM) and REGULUS (maternal grandsire of ECLIPSE). The Godolphin was so named when acquired by the Earl of Godolphin and he was considered to be an unusually large Eastern sire: of the 1 in 7 winners from the mid-18th century that stood 15 hh or

The Godolphin Arabian *by Stubbs.* (Fotomas)

more, well over half were by Godolphin or his sons.

THE FAMOUS OFFSPRING

ECLIPSE is perhaps the most famous racehorse of all time, winning 26 major races in his career, 18 of them between May 1769 and October 1770, including the Silver Cup 11 times. He was never beaten in a race. He was by MARSKE (who also stood at Bisterne in Hampshire, to improve the New Forest ponies) out of SPILETTA and was foaled in 1764, the year of a solar eclipse (hence his name). After his death his whole body was measured in immaculate detail by St Bel, the founder of the College of Veterinary Surgeons, and from the records it seems that the chestnut was a long, low horse, with hips considerably higher than withers, and with a heart weighing about 14 lb (6.3 kg). He was bred by the Duke of Cumberland and sold for 75 guineas to a Smithfield salesman who kept racehorses at Mickleham, Surrey, not far from Epsom. The salesman quite quickly sold him on to Colonel O'Kelly for 1,750 guineas! But it was a good bargain: Eclipse won a great deal for his new owner and eventually no one would compete against him. He therefore retired to stud until he died in 1789.

MATCHEM, foaled 1748, traced his line back to both THE BYERLY TURK and THE GODOLPHIN ARABIAN. He was bred by John Holon of Carlisle and sold to Fenwick of Bywell, Northumberland, as a foal. He had many famous wins and claimed many records – for example he ran Newmarket's Beacon course (4 miles 1 furlong 138 yards) in 7 min 20 sec, carrying 8 st 7 lb. It was even claimed he had run a mile in one minute!

HEROD, foaled 1758, was originally called King Herod. He was a rich bay of beautiful symmetry, bred by the Duke of Cumberland and sold to Sir John Moore. His maternal grandsire was Devonshire Childers. He had many successes at

Newmarket until he burst a blood-vessel in 1766 and was thereafter put to stud. His unfortunate tendency for nose-bleeds was passed down to his offspring.

DEVONSHIRE CHILDERS, also called FLYING CHILDERS, was a chestnut with a white nose and four white legs, bred by Mr Childers near Doncaster and sold to the Duke of Devonshire. A son of THE DARLEY ARABIAN, he was never beaten in a race and some fantastic speeds were claimed for him, none of them too precise as the watches of the time were not wholly accurate.

FAMOUS WINNERS ON THE FLAT

BLINK BONNY One of only five fillies to win the Epsom Derby (1857), she did so in a record time of 2 min 45 sec, though she was 'a mean looking mare and would not have fetched £50 at Tattersall's, from her appearance alone'.

The present record of 2 min 33.8 sec was set by MAHMOUD in 1936.

DIOMED Chestnut colt owned by Sir Charles Bunbury and winner of the very first Derby. Proved to be a failure at stud in England and was sold for 50 guineas for export to America at the age of 21, where Colonel John Hoomes of Virginia bought him for 1,000 guineas. There must have been something in the American air: Diomed provided a huge boost to American breeding and was one of the 'fathers' of the Turf in the USA. Descendants include LEXINGTON.

GLADIATEUR Also known as the AVENGER OF WATERLOO, this French horse was the first to challenge the supremacy of English Thoroughbreds in the 19th century. Owned by the Count de Lagrange, he had a nine-race winning sequence in 1865 which included the triple crown of the Guineas, the Derby and the St Leger–all in spite of having a grossly enlarged joint on his foreleg as the result of being trodden on as a foal.

Eclipse, who was foaled in 1764 the year of a solar eclipse, and became one of the most celebrated racehorses of all time. (Fotomas)

Man O'War, America's most famous racehorse. (Hulton)

HERMIT Belonged to Mr Henry Chaplin (later Lord Chaplin) and, though he frequently broke blood vessels, he gave Chaplin a Derby win during a snowstorm in 1867 at odds of 66 to 1, giving his owner sweet revenge over the Marquis of Hastings, who had eloped a few years earlier with Chaplin's fiancée and who lost his £100,000 wager against Hermit's win.

LEXINGTON Famous 19th century Kentucky Thoroughbred, a direct descendant of DIOMED. Won his first two races under the name of DARLEY in 1853 and was then renamed after the Kentucky town which is the centre of the famous Blue Grass country, America's prime horse-breeding area. Won four out of five other 4-mile races, setting a new record for the distance at 7 minutes 19¾ seconds, but then became blind and was retired to stud at Woodburn Farm, Kentucky. He was champion sire 16 times and died in 1875, known as the Blind Hero of Woodburn.

MAN O'WAR America's most famous race-horse, a golden chestnut known affectionately as Big Red. Won 20 of his 21 races. Bought for $5,000 as a yearling in 1918 by Sam Riddle. A hearty eater, he soon became a big horse with a big stride of 28 ft. He simply loved running and it was very hard to hold him at the start. Raced for two years, setting five record times, and was then retired to stud because such excessively high weights were imposed on him. In 23 years at stud he sired 386 foals which won some 1,300 races between them (including BATTLESHIP at the Grand National). Before the great horse died in 1947, his devoted old groom, Will Harbutt, showed him to about half a million people, always leading him out with the words: 'Ladies and gemmun, this is Man O'War. He's the mostest hoss there ever was.'

PHAR LAP Great galloping Australian gelding, another 'big red' and still remembered with great affection more than 50 years after his mysterious death in Mexico in 1932. He won 14 consecutive races, including the 1930 Melbourne Cup. His body was returned to Australia: his heart is now preserved in Canberra, his skin in Melbourne, and his skeleton in New Zealand, where he was bred.

SECRETARIAT Another Big Red chestnut and almost as beloved today as that other Big Red, Man O'War. Winner of the American Triple Crown in 1973. Set record times for the Kentucky Derby (1 minute 59.4 seconds, 1¼ miles) and for the Belmont Stakes (2 minutes 24 seconds for the mile), and broke or equalled three other track records. Retired to stud in 1973 after earning $1.3 million in a 16-month racing career.

STEEL DUST First of the American quarter-horse sires, foaled 1843, and the fastest of his kind in the 1850s. 15 hh bay stallion, powerful sprinter. Resident of the Texan town of Lancaster when he was challenged to a match race in 1855 against the bigger

MONMOUTH in the small town of McKinney (population 500): 10,000 turned up to watch, and to bet very heavily indeed. By then aged 12, Steel Dust looked gaunt and sleepy; the smug McKinney locals bet heavily on Monmouth as a cert but the Lancaster folk knew better and put their all on their ribby horse – money, land and livestock. He won by three lengths and brought economic ruin to McKinney!

CHARIOT AND HARNESS RACING

Chariot racing is a very ancient equestrian sport. The chariot was familiar in ancient Egypt, Mesopotamia, ancient Greece and Rome, and there are many artistic representations of horse-drawn chariots in the ancient world, typically in Thebes tomb paintings about 1400 BC, though in Mesopotamian art of the second and third millennia BC the chariots are more often drawn by asses or perhaps by onagers.

About 774 BC the Greeks held

Chariot racing was a popular ancient sport. (Fotomas)

their first Olympian Games. Nearly a century later, horse-racing was introduced as a major event in the Games: by the 25th Olympiad chariot-racing became and remained the main test of horse speed and endurance in the Grecian arena, though mounted racing was permitted in the 33rd Olympiad, and mule racing and loose-horse racing later on. The chariot course was built in an arena 1,600 feet long by 400 feet wide, divided by an earthen bank with a pillar at each end, and the race was run over about 4 miles. As it involved several very sharp turns around the pillars, the skill of the charioteer was as important as the qualities and speed of his horses. There were often as many as 40 chariots taking part.

In Rome chariot racing became a major circus attraction. The chariots lined up obliquely at the start and attempted seven circuits. The horses, usually driven by slaves, came from Spain, Sicily and Cappadocia. The epic film *Ben Hur* showed chariot racing at its most hair-raising: the film was based on a Lew Wallace novel (1880) in which the horses were Arabians named ALDEBARAN, ANTARES, ATAIR and RIGEL, but in the 1959 film starring Charlton Heston they were highly trained Lipizzaners.

Today's harness racing can be equally dramatic, if less ferocious, and now takes place on organized tracks under strict regulations. It is especially popular in the USA, Australia and New Zealand, but is also important in several European countries. There are two types of harness racing, depending on the gait of the horses: trotting or pacing. Pacers are a recognized type with a natural tendency to 'trot' in a lateral movement, with the legs on the same side striding in unison rather than in diagonal pairs as in a normal trot.

In the 19th century, trotting matches were the national sport in America just as flat racing was Britain's sport. Oliver Wendell-Holmes, a born-and-bred New Englander, said that the running horse was a gambling toy but the trotting horse was useful, and that 'horse-racing is not a republican institution, but horse-trotting is'.

FAMOUS TROTTERS AND PACERS

DAN PATCH Big brown pacing stallion, foaled in Indiana in 1896. Won every race in 1901 and 1902, and was sold in 1902 for a record $60,000. Then went on exhibition tours, travelling 10,000 miles in 1904 when he was seen by 60,000 people. Held nine world records and retired undefeated in 1909. An easygoing horse, he was much loved

Flora Temple, trotting queen.

by the public and became a household word, giving his name to a wide range of products such as cigars, chewing tobacco, toys, sleds, pillows, ladies' scarves and washing machines – there was even a dance called the Dan Patch Two-Step. He died in 1916, and his by then very rich owner died the following day.

DEXTER Great trotter who lowered FLORA TEMPLE's mile record by more than two seconds in 1867 to 2 minutes 17¼ seconds. He was as fast under the saddle as pulling a sulky. (In the old days, trotters and pacers were raced under the saddle, but the practice became less common as sulkies became more lightweight and better in design. Saddle trotting faded out in America, though it is still seen in Europe.)

FLORA TEMPLE The all-time queen of the trotting matches. Foaled 1845 at Langerford, Oneida County, New York, she was by a 'one-eyed Kentucky hunter' out of Madame Temple, a clever and fast-trotting mare who was said to be by a spotted Arabian sire. Flora Temple was a rich 'blood' bay with black points and no white; she stood 14 hh and had a powerful, wiry frame and a light Arab head. She was also bob-tailed, and was possibly the 'bob-tailed nag' of the song *De Camptown Races* (1850).

Used as a livery horse for two years before her extraordinary potential was developed by Mr G E Perrin of New York City, she won her first public match in 1850 and hardly ever lost a race in her entire career to June 1860, when she

was still in her prime at 15 years old, having achieved a record mile in 2 minutes 19¾ seconds on the Kalamazoo course in Michigan and 2 miles in 4 minutes 50½ seconds at Long Island. She was the first harness horse to run a mile in less than 2 minutes 20 seconds.

GOLDSMITH MAID Foaled 1857, this beautiful bay granddaughter of HAMBLETONIAN was called 'the trottin'st mare in history'. She broke the world trotting record for the mile seven times, including a run of 2 minutes 14 seconds at the age of 17, and she didn't stop racing until she was 20 years old.

GREYHOUND Foaled 1932 and acclaimed as America's greatest trotter, this gelding broke 14 world records between 1934 and 1940, when 'The Gray Ghost' was retired and exhibited – a white horse with red halter, red ribbons and even his hooves painted red.

HAMBLETONIAN Foaled in 1840, a great-grandson of MESSENGER. Purchased as a foal with his dam for a total of $124 by William Rysdyk of Goschen, New York. Not particularly fast under harness but his descendants have monopolized harness racing ever since, and he is the father of the modern Standardbred.

MARSHLAND SHALES Foaled 1802, barely 15 hh at his peak, a chestnut who was almost dun, with an immense crest. Never beaten and could carry 12 stone (76.2 kg) 17 miles in 58 minutes. Descendant of FLYING CHILDERS. Marshland Shales was described by a very old man in George Borrow's *Lavengro* as 'the best mother in England' and the gentle little horse could still trot 20 miles in the hour when half-blind in his old age, making grown men weep to see him.

MESSENGER Foaled 1780 in England, this big grey Thoroughbred was exported to America at the age of eight after a good racing career.

Descendants of his and of JUSTIN MORGAN developed into the American trotter now called Standardbred, specially for harness racing. More than 90% of today's Standardbred pacers and trotters are from Messenger via his great-grandson HAMBLETONIAN, and one of them was America's famous MAN O'WAR.

NIATROSS Said to be the greatest Standardbred in American harness-racing history and had a habit of shattering world records. Big bay colt, won 37 out of 39 races, including Triple Crown in 1980 (Cane Pace, Little Brown Jug, Messenger Stakes), then retired to stud that year after winning his last race, in Florida, in typical style by 17 lengths.

NIHILATOR Foaled 1982, by Niatross out of Margie's Melody. 33 wins in 35 races and holder of world pacing record with a time of 1 minute 49.6 seconds.

RAMBLING WILLIE Foaled 1970, this pacer raced longer, won more purses and broke more records than any other in history. Disabled several times, twice by a bowed tendon. Had won more than a hundred races by the age of 11, and gave a twentieth of his considerable winnings to the Church of Christ in West Mansfield, Ohio: the pastor's daughter owned half the horse and she tithed her earnings to the church's funds. His biography, published in 1981, was entitled *Rambling Willie: The Horse That God Loved.*

SLEEPY TOM Frequent pacing winner in 1878, when he was about ten years old and had already been sold several times, once in exchange for a cheap watch, a bottle of whisky and a three-year-old colt. He set the world's mile pacing record at 2 minutes 12¾ seconds in 1879. He was driven by his owner Stephen C Phillips entirely by voice: the horse was completely blind!

EQUESTRIAN GAMES

WAR GAMES

The Great Horse which was developed in medieval times was essentially a war horse: not only did it carry its bulky, armoured rider but also it was a stallion bred and trained for violence. Big, slow and lumbering, it was as irresistible as a tank, and it was sometimes fitted with homicidal shoes which could trample men to death.

But when firearms superseded lances, these cumbersome beasts became something of a joke and the war horse was demoted to hauling artillery and supplies, a role in which it reached its peak – or its Waterloo – in the First World War when 1,212,177 horses were purchased by the British army (61% of them draught horses), 468,322 of which were bought in Britain. During that terrible war the French army at home lost more than half a million horses.

In the Second World War, although the Polish cavalry was awesome in its bravado and skill, the day of the horseman was over. Even the matchless Poles could only be suicidal against the iron horses of Germany's tanks. Little fragments of horsemanship struggled on the war's fringes – the Cossacks in the snow, and some Japanese cavalry in China and Manchuria, for example. Yet about 10,000 hunters and riding horses had been taken for the British Army's work, mostly in the Middle East with Yeomanry regiments. Many of the hunters left at home during the war had to be destroyed because of lack of forage, or scraped by on a ration of grass, as corn was not available for horses. Thereafter the horse almost ceased to be used in the British Army at all, except for displays.

SKILL-AT-ARMS

The brutality of war has always been offset by the games men play to keep themselves and their horses fighting fit.

BAZ-KIRI A Mongolian game in which teams try to seize the carcass of a goat and carry it to a goal. The game can continue for hours over very rough terrain: a great test of skill, agility and endurance.

TILTING Charging at full gallop to plunge a lance tip through a dangling ring.

QUINTAIN Beheading or piercing an effigy at the gallop.

TENT-PEGGING Taking a grounded tent-peg with a lance, at speed, within a series of tests including tilting, jumping, swordwork and shooting.

JOUSTING Duels between well-armoured opponents charging with lances at full speed with the intention of unsaddling each other, to rules laid down in the middle of the 11th century by the French knight, Geoffroi de Preuilly of Touraine. In 1559 Henry II of France was accidentally killed in a jousting match when a freak lance pierced his eye, and thereafter the

Tent-pegging on barebacked horses by the 11th Hussars in Bengal. (Billie Love)

The early days of polo – Persian v. Turkish players. (ILN)

fashion began to swing in favour of less harmful carousels in which cavalry teams performed intricate manoeuvres. Such carousels were very popular in 17th-century Vienna: they included horse ballets, quadrilles on horseback or in carriages, and other 'dances', and led to the musical rides and drives still seen today. In America a carousel is quite another type of equine entertainment: it is a merry-go-round, on which the mounts are painted hobby horses rising and falling to the music – and that is about as far as you can get from the war-game chargers of old!

GYMKHANAS

The Anglo-Indian word 'gymkhana' means 'a field-day on horseback' and the idea originated in India. The events were excuses for soldiers to have a 'jolly' on non-polo days and the mounted games were intended to be challenging but fun and to involve everyone in the competing, including wives and girlfriends. The object was that everyone should 'leave the touchline for the arena'.

Gymkhanas began in the 1880s and the mounts included camels, donkeys, mules and bicycles as well as horses, with all sorts of buggies, traps and tongas for variety.

Gymkhanas soon came to Britain and were initially organized by mounted regiments and polo clubs for the soldiers but they gradually became village affairs, increasingly for children rather than adults, with regular programmes of bending races, potato races, musical chairs and chase-me-charlies. In 1929 the Pony Club was formed and many of its branches ran gymkhanas. Then

in 1957 the Duke of Edinburgh inspired the first Mounted Games Championships, with its finals at Harringay. The horse of the soldier had finally become the play pony of children.

POLO

There are records of polo by Eastern poets and historians back to 500 and 600 BC in Persia (which is now Iran). It is a game of the East, played throughout Asia from Japan and China to Mongolia, and it was taken to India by Moslem and Chinese invaders. The word 'polo' comes from the Tibetan 'pulu', a woody root from which the ball was made, and in Persia the game was called *chaugan* (mallet).

The game has only been played outside Asia since the 1860s or 1870s, thanks to the enthusiasm of 19th-century British tea-planters and army officers serving in India. The first white man's polo club was formed in 1859 at Silchar, capital of Cachar, where the tea-planters learned the game by playing with the locals on their little kangjai ponies. It was the national game in Cachar and also in Manipur, on the North East Frontier, where army officers took it up, as well as in the mountains of the north west between Chitral and Tibet.

MODERN POLO: AN EARLY CHRONOLOGY

1859 Silchar Club formed and rules drawn up: 9 riders per side (later reduced to 7 and then to 4).

1869 Introduced to England by officers from 9th Lancers, 10th Hussars, 1st Life Guards, Royal Horse Guards – eight-a-side on Hounslow Heath. 10th Hussars in England tried it with hockey sticks and a cricket bat.

1874 Hurlingham became headquarters of English polo; first set of rules formalized the following year. Indian Polo Association formed with own rules.

1876 Pony height limit in India 13.2 hh; in England 14 hh. First introduced to USA by James Gordon Bennett. The game soon spread to Argentina, Australia and New Zealand, and then France, the first continental polo nation.

1886 Westchester Cup founded: first international polo matches (Britain and USA).

1893 Champion Cup of Argentina founded. Argentine players began to visit England. National Pony Society founded to promote breeding of polo ponies.

1914 English polo reached its zenith between Boer War and 1914: 60 clubs in England, often using Indian and Argentine ponies. Many visiting Argentine teams: transatlantic transport cost only £6 per pony on the Old City Line.

1928 First Cup de las Americas at Meadowbrook, won by America (and again in 1932).

1936 Argentina won open polo tournament at the Olympic Games in Berlin and won Cup de las Americas.

1937 The Ashton Brothers team from Goulbourn, Australia, won the Champion Cup in England.

1939–45 Polo grounds at Hurlingham, Ranelagh and Roehampton became wartime allotments. The all-time great American player, Tommy Hitchcock, was killed during the war flying a fighter plane over England. Prime foreign grounds by the end of the war included Meadowbrook at Long Island (13 grounds for rich city businessmen and their sons) with others in California and Florida. Egypt's Gezireh Sporting Club had three beautiful grounds at Cairo and a small one at Alexandria. In India there were major winter tournaments in Delhi, Bombay and Calcutta.

1950 The game was revived in post-war England by Lord Cowdray at Midhurst in Sussex. During the 1950s there were perhaps 500 regular English players, a thousand Americans – and 5,000 in Argentina, which became the leading polo-playing country in the world, reigning supreme from 1946 onwards.

ARGENTINE POLO PONY TRAINING

Polo was first played in the Argentine on the huge English-owned estancias by the employees (peons) and their masters. Polo pony minders were called *petizeros* and the special pony trainer was known as the *domador*. At first the mounts were of the original small Indian pony type, the Petzo, which was stocky, cobby and short-legged. Then came the Criollo, influenced by pure Arabian and Barb stallions introduced by the Spaniards.

In early training use was made of the *bocado*, a strip of rawhide in place of a snaffle. This traditional gaucho method involved winding the strip twice through the pony's mouth under the tongue, fixing it firmly behind the tusks, and tying the ends through two small rings under the chin groove, then attaching rawhide reins. The peons, like the gauchos, rode with tapering rawhide leathers fixed to small, compressed lumps of hide or wooden discs which were slipped between the rider's toes, Indian style. Newly caught free-ranging ponies were mounted and allowed to buck and then to gallop many miles over the wide open plains until they were exhausted and effectively 'broken'.

RODEOS

Rodeos (the word is Spanish for 'round-up') are the natural games for cowboys in the USA and Australia. They began as informal events at the end of the annual trail-drives, where the men could show off their cowboy skills. By the 1870s more formal events were being staged in Wyoming and Kansas, and in 1883 prizemoney was offered for steer-roping in Pecos, Texas. In 1887, for the first time, charges were made for admission to a rodeo, in Denver, Colorado.

RODEO EVENTS

Calf-roping (rope, tie and prepare for branding).
Saddle bronco riding from a starting chute (10 seconds).
Bareback bronco riding (8 seconds).
Bull riding (8 seconds).

Steer-wrestling or bull-dogging.
Barrel racing for cowgirls (cloverleaf bending race).
Cutting out a calf or steer from the 'herd'.
Team roping.
Chuckwagon racing.
Rodeo Queen parade.
Trick riding and fancy roping.
Musical rides.
Clowns (with a serious role – to distract broncos and bulls from a fallen rider).
Cowhide race (1 man pulled along the ground riding on a mat of cowhide).

WORLD HORSEBACK FESTIVALS

ALL-AMERICAN FINALS at Oklahoma City.

APPLEBY HORSE FAIR, Cumbria, England: Traditional gypsy fair in June.

CALGARY STAMPEDE, Canada: World's largest professional rodeo, with four-horse chuckwagon races, musical chairs, roping, whip-cracking, wild-cow milking contests and pancake breakfasts.

CAVALCADES OF VIL DE MOINHOS, Viseu, Portugal: Grand parade of horsemen through the town to commemorate victory of millers over farmers in a 17th century drought.

CAVALRY FESTIVAL, Kairouan, Tunisia: Traditional Arab horse races and dances.

CHEYENNE FRONTIER DAYS, Wyoming: The most famous rodeo in the USA, started in 1897, and includes parades, carnivals and square dancing.

DENVER STOCK SHOW Colorado's biggest rodeo included.

FEAST OF ST PETER AND ST PAUL, Buskett, Mdina, Malta: Ancient harvest festival including bareback races.

JOUST OF THE QUINTANA, Ascoli Piceno, Italy: Historical pageant dating from 13th century.

JOUST OF THE SARACENS, Arezzo, Italy: Procession in 14th-century costume in the Piazza Grande; horsemen battling for the Golden Lance.

PADSTOW 'OBBY 'ORSE MAY DAY, Cornwall, England: Stylized 'horse' dressed in black prancing through the streets – old pagan festival.

PENDLETON ROUND-UP, North America: Oregon's major rodeo.

SHRIMP FESTIVAL, Oosduinkerke, Belgium: Traditional shrimp harvest by fishermen on horseback riding into sea to collect their catch which is then cooked and sold on the beach – big procession in town the following day.

SINJ EQUESTRIAN EVENT, Yugoslavia: Medieval tournament with jousting knights, commemorating 18th-century victory over the Turks.

SOMA NOMAOI, Hibarigahara, Haramachi, Japan: A thousand riders in ancient armour, and men in white costumes trying to catch wild horses on the plains.

TISSA HORSE FESTIVAL, Morocco: Hundreds of riders in full finery competing for prizes.

TUSCANY BAREBACK RACE, Palio, Siena, Italy: Historic 2-minute race and spectacular processions in the medieval Piazza del Campo.

HUNTING

First of all men hunted on foot, but the use of horses for hunting began to creep into ancient Greece. Arrian wrote: 'Give me young men who are not too stout; for the hunter must mount the noble horse amid the rocks and leap ditches.'

Oppian said that a hunter-charger 'must have size and substance and well-knit limbs; a small head carried high, with a neck arching like the plume on a helmet; forehead broad, forelock thick and curly; eye clear and fiery; a broad chest, a back with a double chine; a good full tail; muscular thighs and fine, clean legs, pastern sloping, hoof rising high, close-grained and strong'. These were apparently the qualities found in Tuscan, Armenian, Achaean and the famous Cappadocian horses used for hunting wild beasts or as war chargers.

For many centuries, prey in Europe included hares, wolves, wild boar, bears and various members of the deer family. The Celts were already great hunters on horseback and Britain was famed for its hunting dogs even before the Roman invasion. But hunting became the sport of nobility, and in 1387 Gaston de Foix said: 'Hunting causeth a man to eschew the seven deadly sins. Men are better when riding, more just and understanding.' In 1735 William Somervile described the chase as 'the Sport of Kings; Image of War, without its guilt'.

The fox has been hunted in Britain for more than 300 years but fox-hunting did not become really popular until the early 19th century, after the famous William 'Flying' Childe had, in the late 18th century, introduced the art of riding *to* hounds rather than after them.

FOX-HUNTING RECORDS

EARLIEST FOXHOUND PACKS The Old Charlton Hunt (later Goodwood) in West Sussex, the Duke of Monmouth and Lord Grey of Werke at Charlton, Sussex, and the Duke of Buckingham in north Yorkshire owned packs which were entered to fox only during the reign of Charles II (1660–85).

ARF ARF ARF

LARGEST PACK The Duke of Beaufort's at Badminton since 1786; it once had 120 couple.

LONGEST SPAN AS MASTER The 10th Duke of Beaufort, MFH from 1924 until his death in 1984. He hunted his hounds on 3,895 days between 1920 and 1967.

LONGEST HUNT BY DISTANCE Squire Sandys, in 1743, from Holmbank, north Lancashire, to Ulpha in Cumbria – nearly 80 miles in about 6 hours.

LONGEST HUNT BY DURATION Charlton Hunt of West Sussex (now extinct) on 26 January 1738 – 10 hours 5 minutes (7.45 a.m. from East Dean Wood to 5.50 p.m. kill – 57¼ miles).

MOST WIDESPREAD HUNTER J N P Watson, hunt correspondent for *Country Life*, hunted with 257 different packs of foxhounds, staghounds and hare hounds in Britain, Ireland, Europe and the United States, 1969–88.

The golden age of hunting was 1850–1914: no wire, fewer railways, no tarmac or motor vehicles, less use of artificial fertilizers, plenty of big estates, long masterships – and less taxes. The Second World War was potentially disastrous for hunting because of the great difficulties in feeding hounds and horses, but farmers and the Ministry of Agriculture came to the rescue.

SHOW-JUMPING

Since the 18th-century land enclosures, hunters have needed the ability to jump over fences, hedges and ditches, and that ability has been encouraged in the show-ring in recent years. The Ancient Greeks would be amazed.

1788 First mention of jumping in any cavalry manual (a French one).

1865 First competitions for wide leaps and high leaps at Royal Dublin Society's annual show, Ireland. Similar events in Russia, and in Paris the following year.

1875 Saumur Cavalry School, France, included jumping in its *Haute École* display.

1876 First officially recorded show-jumping in England at the five-day Agricultural Show at Islington. Points awarded solely for style, judged by a Master of Foxhounds.

1900 Second modern Olympic Games in Paris included three jumping events – High, Long, Prize. The Belgian riders Haegemann and Van Langendonck were prominent.

1901 First officially recorded international show-jumping, in Turin. (German versus Italian army officers.)

1907 First International Horse Show at Olympia, London, England, directed by the Earl of Lonsdale, including high and wide leaps. with considerable prizemoney. Dominated by Belgium and Holland.

1912 First permanent inclusion of equestrian events in Olympics, at Stockholm, Sweden, but exclusively for the military. Complicated new rules. Individual jumping, team jumping, dressage, and the 'Military' (later Three-Day Event).

1921 Foundation of Fédération Equestre Internationale (FEI). Members were Sweden, France, Belgium, Denmark, Italy, Japan, Norway and USA; Germany joined later that year, and Switzerland the following year. Britain joined in 1925.

1923 Foundation of British Show Jumping Association, with Lord Lonsdale as its president and Colonel V D S Williams (father of Dorian) as its secretary.

1930 Jack Talbot-Ponsonby won King George V Cup for first of three times. Thereafter the sport of show-jumping slumped in Britain because it became monotonous, with lack of inspiration in creating jumps.

1944 Mike Ansell had been a prisoner-of-war with Nat Kindersley and Bede Cameron and they devised plans to improve British show-jumping. Ansell became chairman of BSJA on his repatriation in 1944. Birth of the White City shows, with early victories to Nat Kindersley, Colonel Harry Llewellyn and Douglas Bunn.

1948 First post-war Olympics, held in England, with Wembley the venue for show-jumping. Britain won its first Olympic show-jumping medal – a team bronze.

FAMOUS JUMPERS

ARETE One-eyed horse ridden by Humberto Mariles of Mexico, winning the individual gold at the 1948 Olympics.

FLANAGAN Gave Pat Smythe a hat-trick (1961–3) with the European women's championship established in 1957 (Pat Smythe won that first one, too). In 1956 the duo went to Stockholm, where she was the first woman rider to compete in the Olympics as part of the British team. They also went to Rome together four years later.

FOXHUNTER First horse to win the King George V Gold Cup three times, with Colonel Harry Llewellyn. Also clinched the gold for the British team at Helsinki in 1952. Foxhunter was by the premium stallion Erehwemos (read its name backwards!) and had a Clydesdale mare as his grandmother.

HALLA Helped Hans-Gunter Winkler win two successive Men's World Championship titles in the 1950s. Also the individual gold at Stockholm in 1956. One of the greatest mares ever seen in show-jumping.

NIZEFELLA Ridden by Wilf White – had an action which was often described as 'pig-rooting' but very popular character with the public. One of the best Nations Cup horses in the world, he had started life as a plough horse in Lincolnshire: he had Shire blood in him.

STROLLER Delightful little pony of character ridden by Marion Mould (née Coakes). They gained a silver at the Mexican Olympics in 1968. In 1965 the famous partnership became the youngest rider and smallest horse to win the Queen Elizabeth II Cup, and then took the first Women's World Championship at Hickstead.

SUNSALVE Was the young David Broome's horse when he went to the Rome Olympics as a newcomer, and had been ridden to victory by Broome in the King's Cup within a fortnight of their first trial ride together. Broome remembers

69

Wilf White on Nizefella at the 1954 Horse of the Year Show. (Hulton)

Sunsalve as the most fantastic Olympic performer he ever rode, though he also rode the brilliant MISTER SOFTEE. Of his many other rides his favourite was little SPORTSMAN.

JUMPING RECORDS

HIGHEST

1893 ROSEBERY cleared 6 ft 11¾ in at the Chicago Horse Show.

1937 Record stood at 7 ft 6½ in by SWANK (owned by Fred Foster and ridden by 'Curly' Beard's brother Donald) at Olympia.

1937 JIMMY BROWN, a liver chestnut, cleared 7 ft 4 in at

Olympia, giving the record for a woman rider to the Lady Wright (née Margery Avis Bullows).

1949 HUASO, ridden by Captain Alberto Morales of Chile, cleared 8 ft 0¼ in at Santiago, to claim the still unbeaten official FEI record high jump.

1978 LASTIC, a grey gelding ridden by Nick Skelton, cleared 7 ft 7⁵/₁₆ in at Olympia, the British record.

1982 REGAL FLIGHT cleared 7 ft at Dublin to give Michael Whitaker the record high jump riding bareback.

LONGEST

1847 Claims made for 39 ft by CHANDLER and 37 ft by PROCEED,

but not substantiated. In the 1970s a record of a mere 27 ft 6¾ in was claimed in Johannesburg.

PERPENDICULARS

In 1919 there was something of a craze for 'jumping down perpendicular heights on horseback'. Captain Julio de Oliveira, Instructor of Equitation at the Portuguese Military Riding School, described and photographed some hair-raising examples in *The Field*. At the riding school at Torres Novas there was a vertical descent of 15 ft (4.5 m) which each cadet had to negotiate several times, and at nearby Charneca de Atalaya was another 15 ft vertical drop measured from ground-level to the water level of a river at the foot of the cliff – an added hazard for the hundreds of cadets who attended the school.

The Captain gave instructions on how riders should be positioned during such precipitous descents, the rider with his body inclined forward. 'Cadets are taught in the riding school to assume this position, which is surely the one which should be taught at all schools of military equitation. The rider should gallop and jump with his horse; it is only so that he obtains the necessary solidity and flexibility of seat which enables him to get the most out of his horse, and this has led all first-rate foreign horsemen, whether English, French, Italian, Belgian, or Portuguese, to abandon the old academical position for the modern elastic seat which permits the rider to deal with obstacles in perfect accord with the movements of his horse – in other words, to play an active and not a passive part in the performance.'

EVENTING

1912 First Olympic three-day event at Stockholm, Sweden.

1948 Olympics in London, England, with three-day event at Aldershot organized by the newly formed British Horse Society.

1949 Duke of Beaufort initiated the three-day event at Badminton, England ('Olympic Horse Trials'), in response to disappointing British results at 1948 Olympics; original aim was to produce international and Olympic teams.

1955 European Championships at Windsor, England. 17th was young Sheila Willcox on HIGH AND MIGHTY; she was to win three successive Badmintons in the late 1950s and was first lady champion at Copenhagen, Denmark, on the same horse.

1956 Britain won first team gold at Stockholm Olympics.

Originally the Three-Day Event was an exercise for military chargers and was known as 'the Military', designed to test a horse's ability to cover long distances at a good speed over open country, surmounting whatever obstacles and hazards there might be.

As the military involvement decreased at the Olympic Games, the event became known as the Concours Complet. Between the wars it settled into roughly the pattern seen today:

Dressage
Speed and endurance, including two courses taken at trot or slow canter, a galloping steeplechase course and a galloping cross-country course with fixed solid obstacles
Show-jumping.

Badminton was won six times by Lucinda Green (née Prior-Palmer) from 1973 to 1984, riding BE FAIR, WIDE AWAKE, GEORGE, KILLAIRE, REGAL REALM and BEAGLE BAY.

ENDURANCE AND LONG-DISTANCE RIDING

Typical tests in endurance are rides of 75 or 100 miles. The sport began in its present form in the mid-1950s in the USA: the first Tevis Cup in 1955 followed the Gold Rush trail over the Sierra Nevadas, starting at Lake Tahoe and finishing at Auburn, California – 100 miles in one day. The idea spread to Australia in the 1960s, and in the following decade to Britain, South Africa, New Zealand, West Germany and other countries. Endurance is open to any breed or type of horse or pony, and riders range from small children to adults. The stages are:

SHORT-DISTANCE PLEASURE RIDES for novices, non-competitive, 15–30 miles.

COMPETITIVE TRAIL-RIDES with speed brackets: the prime factor in judging is the horse's overall fitness before, during and after the competition. 25–60 miles in one day in Britain; up to 100 miles in 3 days in USA.

ENDURANCE RIDING from 25 to 130 miles in a day, with veterinary checks every 15–20 miles. Winner is fastest fit horse over the distance. Some can cover 100 miles of tough terrain in less than 12 hours, or 50 miles in about 5 hours.

1966 First Tom Quilty Endurance Ride (100 miles, Australia) won by the Arabian stallion SHALAWI in 11 hours 24 minutes, with Gabriel Stecher riding bareback.

1976 Great American Horse Race from New York to Sacramento in California – 3,000 miles on two mounts (one led as the other was ridden). Began during Memorial Day weekend in May, scheduled to finish on Labour Day in September. The winner, Verl Norton, rode a mule!

1986 A British team won the world championship for endurance in Rome, Italy.

SOME VERY LONG RIDES

Mr Shafto on 27 June 1759 undertook a race against time in which he had to ride 50 miles on an unlimited number of horses in two successive hours. He succeeded in 1 hour 49 minutes 17 seconds, using ten horses (four of them twice), making an average rate of 2 minutes per mile.

Squire George Osbaldeston, Member of Parliament for Retford, rode 200 miles over the Newmarket round course, using 28 horses, and including 1 hour 22 minutes 56 seconds for stoppages, in 8 hours 42 minutes, averaging 23 mph.

CHAMPION CRABBET covered 300 miles in 52 hours 33 minutes in 1920, carrying 17½ stone.

Mr Thornhill, in 1759, rode from Stilton to London, then back to Stilton, and then to London again (213 miles) in 11 hours 13 minutes.

Henry G. Perry, a stockman from Mollongghip, Victoria, rode 14,021 miles around Australia between 1 May and 4 October 1985, using six horses.

Robert O'Hara Burke rode across Australia and halfway back again on BILLY but at that point he was starving and he shot and ate the horse.

Francis Asbury, a Methodist preacher born in Birmingham, England, rode 264,000 miles in North America from 1771 to 1815 and preached 16,000 sermons on the way.

Ken Northdruft rode a marathon 112 hours 30 minutes at Kingsthorpe, Queensland, Australia, from 31 August to 4 September 1985.

Gary Bourne and David Ward rode a record 179.25 miles in armour around Kent, England, from 10 to

14 July 1988, with a riding time of 41 hours 5 minutes.

Dick Turpin, highwayman, rode 180 miles from London to York on BLACK BESS – in fiction. In fact the real Richard Turpin probably made no such ride and he was hanged in 1739 for horse-stealing.

Paul Revere, silversmith, 1735–1818, undertook a famous American ride on a small chestnut Narragansett Pacer mare on 18 April 1775, from Charleston. He was captured halfway between Lexington and Concord (Massachusetts) at 2 a.m. on the 19th, and a British soldier rode off on the mare.

In the 19th century a purebred mustang was raced from Galveston, Texas, to Rutland in Vermont (1,800 miles) against much larger and faster horses, and came in a fortnight ahead of its rivals.

Still in 19th-century America, a North West Mounted Police constable rode 132 miles from Regina to Wood Mountain Post in a heavy stock saddle weighing 42 lb (19 kg), without changing horses, and achieved the journey in daylight – not an unusual feat when MP constables and cowboys often rode more than 100 miles a day.

Kit Carson and three Mexicans rode 600 miles from Los Angeles to San Francisco without changing horses, taking 6 days.

In the 1860s, American Pony Express riders averaged 9 miles an hour over 25-mile stages, with two minutes to change horses, and covered a round trip of 70–100 miles twice a week.

Lady Godiva almost qualifies for an 'endurance' ride. In England in 1040 she besought Leofric, Earl of Mercia and Lord of Coventry, to remove certain taxes he had imposed on his tenants. He agreed to do so if she rode naked through the town. She did; he did; and in theory all the townsfolk had the courtesy to remain indoors while she rode by, but a tailor could not resist peeping through his window. He was the original Peeping Tom, and the legend is that he was promptly struck blind.

The American Pony Express en route from the Missouri River to San Francisco. (Mary Evans)

HIGH HORSES

BLACK AGNES (named after Agnes of Dunbar) and ROSABELLE were palfreys ridden by Mary Queen of Scots – Rosabelle was her favourite.

BLACK JACK was a dark chestnut ceremonial gelding who, riderless, followed the coffin of President Kennedy in 1963. In the traditional manner (said to trace back to the Mongols, who would subsequently sacrifice the riderless horse so that it could serve its master in the afterlife) a sheathed sword was strapped to the saddle and boots were placed facing backwards in the stirrups. The same tradition has often been followed in State Funerals in England.

BUCEPHALUS was the famous mount of Alexander the Great, variously described as three-toed and horned – in fact his name meant Ox Head and he would wear golden horns in battle, which might have influenced the unicorn legend. Alexander's successors often showed a horned horse on their coinage, and as late as the 13th century Marco Polo was told by the people of Balasham, in northern Afghanistan, of their rulers' breed of horses which were born with a special mark on the forehead because they were descended from Bucephalus, who had a white star on his forehead. Bred in Thessaly and bought by Philip II of Macedonia for the equivalent of

several thousand pounds, the horse proved uncontrollable until Philip's 12-year-old son Alexander noticed that he was afraid of his own shadow. The boy tamed Bucephalus, who would kneel for him to mount but would never allow anyone else to ride him. Thereafter the black horse accompanied Alexander the Great in all his campaigns and died in action from arrow wounds in the neck when he was 30 in a battle against Rajah Porus at the Jhelum river. In his memory, his master founded the city of Bucephela.

CELER THE SWIFT belonged to the Roman emperor Lucius Verus, who dressed the horse in royal purple, stabled it in the imperial palace, and fed it on almonds and raisins.

COMANCHE was the sole survivor of Custer's cavalry at the Battle of Little Big Horn in 1876. The horse, the mount of Captain Myles Keogh, was badly wounded in several places but survived another 17 years, allowed to wander where he pleased about the forts at which he was posted, his only duties being ceremonial. He died in 1893 and his stuffed body was put on display at the University of Kansas.

COPENHAGEN, grandson of ECLIPSE, was bought as a four-year-old by the Duke of Wellington and was ridden by him throughout the Battle of Waterloo three years later in 1815. The little chestnut stallion was in action from six in the morning until nine in the evening, and when his Duke dismounted

Painting of Marengo, Napoleon's much-loved white Arabian mount. (Fotomas)

two hours later on reaching an inn Copenhagen took a swipe at him! The horse was retired to the Stratfield Saye estate and died in 1836, being buried on the estate with full military honours. His headstone is inscribed:

'God's humble instrument, though meaner clay,
Should share the glory of that glorious day.'

DESIRÉE and MARENGO were Napoleon's white Arabian mounts at Waterloo. MARENGO was his favourite charger and is shown carrying Napoleon across the Alps in various paintings, though in reality a mule was used for that difficult journey. Captured by the English, MARENGO finally died in England in 1829 and his skeleton was displayed at the National Army Museum. One of his hooves was mounted as a silver-lidded snuff-box, inscribed: 'Hoof of Marengo, barb charger of Napoleon, ridden by him at Marengo, Austerlitz, Jena, Wagram, in the Russian campaign, and at Waterloo.'

THE GENERAL was another horse worthy of an inscription. He was the favourite of John Tyler, President of the United States from 1841 to 1845, and the horse was buried at Sherwood, Virginia, with the words:

'Here lies the body of my good horse, The General. For years he bore me around the circuit of my practice and all that time he never made a blunder. Would that his master could say the same.'

INCITATUS was one of the first race-horses and adored by his owner, the infamous Roman emperor Caligula (AD 12–41). On the eve of a race, Incitatus was assured of a good night's sleep by soldiers posted in the area to ensure complete silence, and after his victories Caligula set the horse up in considerable style in a house of his own, with marble stable, marble mangers, gold water buckets, a staff of slaves, and a succession of 'honoured' human guests who (on the whole unenthusiastically) were invited to dine with the horse. In due course Incitatus became a full citizen, a priest and almost a consul.

JAFFA was another of Napoleon's horses: he was a pure Arab, given to Napoleon by Ali Pasha and ridden by him during his victory at Marengo and thereafter on ceremonial occasions. Jaffa was taken to England in 1823 and died at the age of 37 in 1828. There is an elaborate memorial to him at Cranbrook in Kent.

LITTLE SORREL was General 'Stonewall' Jackson's favourite mount, seized at Harper's Ferry in 1861 from a carload of federal cavalry horses. In 1863 the general rode the sturdy little gelding on a reconnoitre at Chancellorsville, Virginia, but unfortunately his own men shot him by mistake, shattering his arm and hand. Little Sorrel bolted – straight towards the enemy Union troops; his rider did manage to turn him in time. Jackson died a week later; the horse lived on for more than twenty years with the general's family, dying in 1886, after which he was stuffed and displayed at the Virginia Military Institute in Lexington.

MORZILLO, or EL MORZILLO, makes a claim to be the first American to be a god. He was one of Cortes' 'cavalry' of a mere 16 horses which captured Mexico in the 16th century: the Indians fled from what they took to be centaurs. The big black Morzillo was ridden again by Cortes on the way to Honduras six years later but became lame with a splinter in his foot: Cortes reluctantly left him with friendly Mayan Indians who decked him with flowers and perfume, and fed him with tender pieces of chicken! When he died, they built a statue of him and began to worship the horse as Tziunchan, the god of thunder and lightning. The life-size statue sat on its haunches like a dog, as described in 1618 by Spaniards arriving at Peten Itza. El Morzillo remained a cult figure for 170 years until the Franciscan monks destroyed his statue, but Indian legend maintains that he can still be seen in the deep, clear lake.

OLD ROWLEY was King Charles II's favourite and a regular sight at Newmarket races in the 17th century – hence the Rowley Mile.

OLD WHITEY was the knock-kneed mount of 'Old Rough and Ready' General Zachary Taylor (so named because his apparel became more and more sloppy as his rank became higher). The short-legged general had to be helped into the saddle and then sat sideways, one leg casually draped over the pommel, with a straw farming hat on his head. His horse matched him well, with its shaggy mane and air of lethargy even in the midst of battle during the Mexican War. Taylor became president in 1849 and Old Whitey had the freedom of the White House lawn.

RONALD was the Earl of Cardigan's chestnut in the charge of the Light Brigade at Balaclava in 1854. The Earl was well ahead of his ill-fated troopers, galloping through the firing to the twelve-gun Russian battery, and he then left his men to continue the fight while he turned Ronald around and rode slowly back along the valley through a hail of shells and bullets. Neither Ronald nor Cardigan suffered so much as a scratch.

SORREL was mean in stature, and blind in one eye. Ridden by William III, the horse stumbled on a molehill in mid-gallop and caused the king's death (apparently from a broken collar-bone).

TUNIS was bought by General Georges Boulanger in 1886 specifically for his first Bastille Day troops review as Minister of War. The big black gelding's handsome prancing enchanted the public and brought instant fame to his rider, who was quickly elected to the Chamber of Deputies. In 1889 Boulanger had the opportunity of staging a *coup d'état* but preferred to leave the country instead, taking with him his mistress – and Tunis. But that first parade became immortalized in the phrase 'the man on horseback' as a term for a military man destined to come forward and save his country by seizing power.

WELL BRED

Several breeds owe their success to royal or noble enthusiasts; others were bred by the monasteries:

ALTER-REAL In 1747 the House of Braganza imported three hundred mares from Jerez in order to set up a national stud at Villa de Portel in southern Portugal's Alentejo province. Later in the century the Alter-Reals gave *haute école* performances in the royal *manège* but the breed nearly vanished in a welter of cross-breeding. It has since been rescued with the help of the Andalusian, and the Alter state stud has been breeding the LUSITANO horse since 1830.

ANDALUSIAN The historic Andalusian probably had its origins in the Barbs introduced from North Africa by the Moorish invaders. For many centuries it was one of the best horses in Europe, except for the Arab, and by the 15th century the Carthusian monks of Jerez were producing beautiful purebred Andalusians. The royal Cordoba stables were founded in 1571 by Philip I. The breed found its way to the new world of America in the 16th century and many of the criollo and mustang herds are descended from this fine horse, either directly or through breeds which it had strongly influenced such as the Neapolitan. Many other breeds relied heavily on the Andalusian for their qualities, especially the Lipitsa (Lipizzaner).

EINSIEDLER Another monastic horse, bred at a Benedictine monastery at Einsiedeln in the Swiss canton of Schwyz. The latter is another name for the breed, which is also known as the Swiss Halfblood and originated from the Anglo-Norman.

FREDERIKSBORG Danish breed, usually chestnut, developed at the Royal Stud set up by Frederik II in 1562 with a stock of Andalusians. The breed originated in the late 19th century from the Stud's stallions crossed with Zealand mares.

HAFLINGER Tyrolean pony, chestnut with light mane and tail, also called the AVELIGNESE – handsome, muscular, trustworthy and of ancient origins, probably tracing to a stallion sent from Burgundy by the German king Louis IV as a wedding gift to his son, the Margrave Louis of Brandenbury, in 1342. Or it might have descended from feral horses abandoned by the Ostrogoths in the 6th century when they fled from Byzantine troops: there is plenty of Arab blood in the pony as well as Noric.

HANOVERIAN England's Hanoverian kings, George I and George II, played a major part in improving this coach horse. In 1735 George II founded the Landgestut at Celle and lightened what had been rather a heavy farm horse.

HOLSTEIN Heavier than the Hanoverian, the Holstein type was bred in the 14th century at the monastic stables of Uetersen (Elbe estuary). It was a good war horse, and later remained big enough to draw artillery and be a cavalry horse. Its ancestry includes Yorkshire Coach-horse blood and Thoroughbred.

KLADRUBER The royal Kladrub stud in Bohemia was founded by the emperor Maximilian II in 1572, with horses of Spanish (Andalusian) and Neapolitan origins, and the breeding has always been strictly controlled. There are two characteristic colours: grey (from the stallion Pepoli, 1764) and black (from the stallion Sacromoso, 1799), and a later contributor, Favory, was also the foundation sire of many Lipizzaners.

LIPIZZANER In 1580 Archduke Charles of Styria founded a stud at Lipitsa, near Trieste, a village now in Yugoslavia but then in Austria. The archduke imported two Andalusian stallions from Spain and Italian mares from Verona, Aquileia and the Po valley, and his breed became famous for supplying the Spanish Riding School founded in Vienna in 1729 by Charles VI. The Lipitsa stud transferred to Piber after the fall of the Austro-Hungarian empire, and was evacuated from there at the end of the Second World War. Most of the Lipizzaners are grey: the six foundation stallions included the greys Maestoso (Andalusian), Pluto (Frederiksborg) and Siglavy (Arab). The foals are born black, however. The other sires were the red roan Favory (Andalusian) and the two Neapolitans, Conversano (brown) and Napolitano (bay).

ORLOV The 18th-century Count Alexei Orlov founded the Khrenov stud and his name was to become synonymous with famous trotting horses. In recognition of his loyalty to Catherine the Great, Orlov was given command of the Russian fleet and was at one stage given an Arab stallion, Smetanka, by a Turkish admiral. Smetanka's son by a dun Danish mare was the stallion, Polkan, who sired a famous trotter, Bars 1, in 1784 – considered to be the breed's foundation sire.

SALERNO Originally derived from local Campanian horses with Andalusian and Arab blood, this medieval cavalry horse was promoted by the Naples king, Charles III, in the late 18th century but it is now rare.

SARDINIAN The early 16th century Catholic king, Ferdinand V,
imported Andalusian stallions to improve the old Sardinian breed which had resulted from the use of Arab horses with small native breeds since the time of the Saracens in Sardinia. Now rare or extinct, the Sardinian was heavily infused with Thoroughbred blood during the 20th century to produce the ANGLO-ARABO-SARDO or Sardinian Anglo-Arab.

TRAKEHNER The Trakehnen stud was founded in Lithuania in 1732 by Friedrich Wilhelm I, and developed the East Prussian military horse from the old SCHWEIKEN or Sweyki. Arab and English Thoroughbred blood gradually created the Trakehner, and a thousand of the breed were taken to West Germany in the aftermath of the Second World War by locals fleeing from the Russian advance. The horses that stayed in East Prussia became the MAZURY or Masuren, which then combined with the POZNAN in 1964 and are now known as the WIELKOPOLSKI in Poland.

HEROES, MASCOTS AND MONUMENTAL MOUNTS

BLIND TOM was a gelding who was said to have hauled every rail of the 1,100 miles of track laid by Union Pacific in the 1860s, starting from Omaha, Nebraska, to link up westwards with the track being laid eastwards by Central Pacific. When the two lines finally met at Promontory Point in Utah, Blind Tom was an unofficial guest of honour at the ceremony of driving a golden spike into the last tie in 1869.

BRIGHAM was 'Buffalo Bill' Cody's best horse in an eight-hour buffalo-killing competition against Billy Comstock, watched by a hundred people who came from St Louis on a special excursion train. Cody, thoroughly drunk on a great

The Trakehner was gradually developed to become one of West Germany's best breeds.

deal of champagne, rode bareback and without a bridle, declaring: 'Old Brigham knows as well as I what I am doing, and sometimes a great deal better.' He won $500 from the match, slaughtering 69 buffalo against Comstock's 46.

CHARLEY was a Comanche pony ridden (more or less) by the artist George Catlin when he crossed five hundred miles of prairie in the 1830s to study the American Indians. Charley spent much of his time slipping his tether during the night and leading Catlin a merry dance. Tired of chasing him, Catlin decided one day to pack up camp and walk off, at which Charley 'neighed very violently', galloped to overtake his master and stood in front of him 'trembling like an aspen leaf' at the thought of being left behind.

GARRYOWEN was a famous Australian horse who died in a fire in 1939. His mistress, Violet Murrell, died trying to save him, and both are remembered in the Perpetual Garryowen Trophy event for women riders more than 18 years old at the Melbourne show: the winner receives the trophy and a sash with a brooch portrait of Violet Murrell.

JUSTIN MORGAN was originally called FIGURE but was later named after his new owner, a music teacher and inn-keeper, who took him to Vermont as a two-year-old in 1795 as a log-hauler. Only 14hh, the chunky little bay was said to have won every weight-pulling contest, quarter-mile sprint and trotting race that he entered, and to have covered a dozen mares a day when at stud. Mr Morgan died in 1798 but his horse continued to work hard for other owners until he died in 1821 after being kicked carelessly in the flank and neglected. His offspring began to attract attention in the 1840s and in 1842 their founding sire was traced as Figure. The breed was officially named the Morgan in 1857, which was when Figure was renamed Justin Morgan. There is a fine statue of the horse, erected on the centenary of his death and given by the Morgan Horse Club to the US Department of Agriculture. In 1961 the Morgan became the state animal of Vermont, and in 1970 the state horse of Massachusetts.

PERSIMMON was the Prince of Wales' Derby winner in 1896. The son of St Simon, he also won the St Leger and the following year the Eclipse Stakes, and was commemorated in an enormous bronze statue at the Royal Stud at Sandringham.

RECKLESS was a war heroine. She was a small Korean racing mare, foaled in 1948 and bought for $250 in 1952 by Lieutenant Eric Pedersen, commander of a US Marine Recoilless ('Reckless') Rifle platoon. Trained to carry ammunition, she was soon promoted to the rank of corporal. In 1953 she made 51 trips up a steep hill in two days under heavy fire, taking more than 9,000 lb (4,000 kg) of ammo to the front, for which she was promoted to sergeant in April 1954, with a citation referring to her 'absolute dependability' which had 'contributed materially to the success of many battles'. The little red mare was retired to Camp Pendleton, California, in 1954 and her story was published the following year.

STEAMBOAT and two other favourite horses of Daniel Webster were buried on his Massachusetts farm standing upright and wearing their halters and shoes. Steamboat, who died in 1838, had been a fine roadster and was described as the *equus celeberrimus* in the inscription on his monument, which, in Latin throughout, ended with the words *'SISTE, VIATOR, MAJOR TE VIATOR HIC SISTIT!'* ['Traveller, pause; A greater traveller than you stops here!']

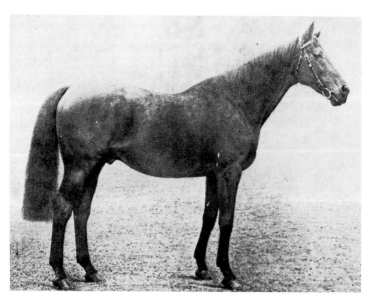

Persimmon, Derby winner in 1896. (ILN)

CULTURED HORSES

HORSES IN ART

'No wonder artists have been inspired by horses. The splendid curves of energy – the neck and the rump, united by the passive curve of the belly, and capable of infinite variation, from calm to furious strength – are without question the most satisfying piece of formal relationship in nature.'

Kenneth Clark (Lord Clark)
Animals and Men, 1977

CAVE PAINTINGS There are Palaeolithic murals of horses in the caves of south-west France and northern Spain at Font-de-Gaume, La Mouthe, Niaux, Les Combarelles, Altamair and, of course, the famous Lascaux caves in the Dordogne discovered in 1940. The animals are not unlike Exmoor ponies – tough and shaggy, with beards and mealy muzzles, and a shock of upright mane like the Tarpan and Przewalsky's horse.

ANCIENT EGYPT The ass as a beast of burden was more often depicted than the horse in early Egyptian art, but by the 14th dynasty stylized horses were shown drawing light war chariots and many of the animals were shallow-girthed and weedy. On the lid of a chest found in his tomb Tutankhamun was depicted driving a hunting chariot.

ASSYRIANS In Mesopotamia the

Ancient Assyrian sculpture of horse's head. (ILN)

Chinese horse of the T'ang period. (ILN)

horse, like many other animals, was admired as a creature of strength and some ferocity: its depictions are much more lifelike than the Egyptian. Many were shown in plunge-gallop drawing their battle chariots; they have well-sprung ribs, hogged manes and plaited tails.

PERSIANS Chariot horses were splendidly sculpted in reliefs at Persepolis (about 5th century BC) but the most superb Persian art was in miniature, especially the illuminated manuscripts of much later centuries, reaching a peak in the 15th and 16th centuries. The oldest Persian horses were shown with roman noses and thick heads but they gradually developed into Arab types.

INDIA The earliest portrayals of horses were as Buddhist symbols on monolithic columns at Sarnath in the reign of the emperor Asoka, about 240 BC, but perhaps the finest Buddhist reliefs were those at Amaravati depicting fighting horses. But, like the Persians, the most beautiful Indian horses are from illuminated manuscripts, especially those created under the Mogul emperors (who brought Persian artists to India), and many of them are delightfully elegant with tiny muzzles and delicate legs but otherwise voluptuously curved.

CHINA Chinese horses were shown as much more solid and chunky than the Arabs. Some bronzes of the Chou dynasty (6th to 3rd century BC) are very solid and strong; those of the Han dynasty are equally powerful, especially a carved stone horse trampling on a barbarian by the tomb of Ho Ch'u-ping (who died about 117 BC). Many other horses of that period seem to be rather violent, or at least very spirited. The famous T'ang pottery horses are typical of the period (7th–10th centuries AD) – very compact and stylized but tense with energy. The emperor T'ai Tsung had carvings of his six favourite chargers on his tomb.

ANCIENT GREECE Greek artists, especially the sculptors, recognized the beauty as well as the power of the horse, and it could be said that no artist since has equalled the Greeks in capturing the exultant energy of the animal, especially in the relief friezes at the Siphnian Treasury in Delphi and above all at the Parthenon.

ROMANS Many Romans copied Greek works of art, and many Greek artists worked in Italy during the 1st century AD. The famous bronze statue of the mounted emperor Marcus Aurelius dates from about 200 BC and was moved to the Capitoline Hill at the request of Michelangelo in 1538. There are early Roman carved horses on the Trajan column (AD 114), and, most famous and exciting of all, there are the wonderful horses of St Mark's in Venice, which are either original 5th century Greek originals or copies made for the emperor Nero for his Golden House in Rome. They were taken from Constantinople to Venice as war booty in 1204.

DARK AGES Monastic artists working on their illuminated manuscripts rarely drew horses from life, or had a feel for the animals – they tend to have rather human expressions on their faces and enormous feet. But the Bayeux Tapestry is very different: here the horses are full of action and look even more realistic than the dying warriors that are falling off and under them. Some parts of the battle scene look like the chaos of falling

horses at the Grand National! No two horses are alike – and there are more than 200 of them worked into the tapestry, including William the Conqueror's Castilian Arab stallion.

MEDIEVAL The manuscript illuminators began to produce some fine miniatures from the early 14th century, especially in what came to be known as Queen Mary's Psalter and in the Duc de Berry's *Book of Hours*. Early in the medieval period, Gothic art was too angular to embrace equine curves but later in the period they began to portray the most beautiful equine creature of all – the fabulous unicorn. This lovely and mysterious white animal is at its best in two late Gothic tapestries: the 'Cloisters' Hunt of the Unicorn at the New York Metropolitan Museum, and the Lady and the Unicorn in the Musée de Cluny in Paris. Domenichino painted a very touching scene of a lady and her unicorn in the Farnese Palace in the 17th century.

Horse studies by Leonardo da Vinci. (Hulton)

ITALIANS Many Italian artists portrayed horses in either paint or sculpture but the horse master was undoubtedly Leonardo da Vinci (1452–1519) who was fascinated by ⁺he animal's beauty and its energy. He made a scientific study of its anatomy and produced superb frescoes and drawings.

17TH CENTURY Da Vinci was a great influence on Rubens who recreated da Vinci's lost fresco of the Battle of Anghiari, in which the horses are as ferocious as the men. Velasquez (1599–1690) really enjoyed painting horses and brought them to life: he enthusiastically studied the elaborate movements taught at the Classical riding schools and tried to capture the spirit of all those leaps, pirouettes, *levades* and *caprioles* – quite a contrast to the stolid, patient Flemish farmhorses of Brueghel.

18TH AND 19TH CENTURIES French artists such as David immortalized Napoleon on his fine white Arab, Marengo, and Theodore Gericault (1791–1824) painted realistic horses, especially the drama of the *Race of the Riderless Horses* through the streets of Rome. But it was Delacroix (1799–1863) who really relished the unbridled passion and rage of horses in his dramatic and often violent paintings of fear and fury. In contrast Rosa Bonheur (1822–1899) painted the colour and fun of the *Horse Fair* and the workaday world of *Horses Threshing Corn* (with ten life-sized horses). Later, Degas caught the spirit of the race track with paintings like *The False Start* (1870) in which the horses are almost balletic; Toulouse Lautrec also painted the race-horse.

BRITISH ARTISTS Francis Barlow, born in the 1620s, painted an early race-horse, but specialist horse artists included John Wootton (1680–1756), James Seymour (1702–52), Sawrey Gilpin (1733–1807), Francis Sartorius (1735–1834), George Morland (1763–1804), Ben Marshall (1767–1835), James Ward (1769–1859), James Pollard (1772–1867), John Ferneley (1782–1860), the Alkens, J F Herring (1795–1865), Sir Alfred Munnings (1878–1959) and others – and, above all, the 18th century artist George Stubbs.

GEORGE STUBBS, who died in poverty in 1805, took his horses so seriously that he spent six years on his Lincolnshire farm dissecting dead animals and drawing them in great detail. The result, published in 1766, was his classic and unique *The Anatomy of the Horse. Including a particular description of the Bones, Cartilages, Muscles, Fascias, Ligaments, Nerves, Arteries, Veins and Glands. In Eighteen Tables, all done from Nature.* His paintings are numerous and well known; they include portraits of many famous racehorses such as Hambletonian, Gimcrack and Whistlejacket.

HERALDRY AND SYMBOLS

The horse is often used in arms and on flags, commonly as a symbol of strength and energy, though in Nigeria it is a symbol of dignity and in Uruguay one of liberty. As well as nations, several American states have horses as their state symbols, and Maryland has jousting as the state sport! Other places have a special relationship with the horse even if it is not used as a symbol. For example, the wild horses and donkeys of Abaco in the Bahamas are a source of national pride; and in Botswana two zebras are depicted as supporters on the presidential standard.

Famous heraldic horses include:

CENTAUR Creature with horse's body but the bust, arms and head of a man, as an emblem of courage and wisdom. A centaur with bows and arrows is a sagittarius, and was the badge of King Stephen as well as becoming a zodiac sign.

SOMA PRANCING HORSE Japanese badge portraying a bucking horse which has been tethered between two stakes and seems to be reacting to its restraint with spirited defiance.

PRANCING BLACK HORSE Seen on the arms of Naples, for example – the charge of Prince Murat. The most familiar black horse in Britain must be the Lloyds Bank symbol. In 1665 Humphrey Stokes, goldsmith and 'keeper of

Horse Frightened By A Lion *by Stubbs.* (Fotomas)

The famous Lloyds Bank black horse symbol.

running cashes', moved from Paternoster Row to Lombard Street and traded at the sign of the Black Horse. Pepys regularly did business with 'little Stokes' both in Paternoster Row and in Lombard Street, where the first of the goldsmith's houses was destroyed in the Great Fire of London in 1666, but the Black Horse soon found new premises in Lombard Street. The sign continued, handed to subsequent generations and to the Bland family who succeeded Stokes, and in 1864 an amalgamation brought the Horse and the name of Lloyds together.

THE WHITE HORSE A galloping white horse was the device of the House of Hanover and became popular as an inn sign during the reigns of George I and George II. In earlier times it was the standard of the ancient Saxons: Hengist and Horsa were semi-legendary leaders of a Saxon war band invited to Kent in 449 to help in the fight against the Picts. The name Hengist is derived from hengst, a stallion, and that of Horsa from horse, and Kent adopted the White Horse as its own emblem. But the origins of the symbol in England could be even older. On several of the downs there are gigantic white horses emblazoned on the slopes, created by removing the turf to reveal the underlying chalk. Perhaps the most famous is at Uffington in Berkshire, measuring about 350 ft (107 m) from nose to tail and traditionally said to commemorate the victory of Alfred the Great over the Danes in 871, though some link it with Hengist and others firmly believe it was

already carved on the hillside before the Roman invasion. Its 'voice' used to be made by the booming sound of the wind against the nearby Blowing Stone, which is now in a village garden. There are 16 other White Horses in England and the one at Westbury in Wiltshire is also very well known.

WINGED HORSE Any symbolic horse can be winged but it is usually PEGASUS, the steed of Apollo, connected with intellectual arts – used, for example, on the arms of the Inner Temple. A badge of the Knights Templar used to show a single horse ridden by two knights, as a symbol of their vow of poverty: the lawyers later transformed the two knights into a pair of wings. Sir John Jervis, Lord St Vincent, was assigned as a crest a pegasus springing from a naval crown, and in the Second World War the British Airborne troops adopted the pegasus as their insignia, with a pale blue winged horse ridden by Bellerophon against a maroon ground.

SEA-HORSES used to look very like the real fish, *hippocampus*, but were also depicted as 'marined' horses whose hindquarters became fish-tails: they often had webbed feet and a dorsal fin as well, and were typically shown being ridden over wave-crests by Neptune (Poseidon) or Boreas. Marined unicorns are seen in German heraldry.

HORSESHOE Although originally the horseshoe was a lucky find in purely practical terms, it soon became a symbol of good luck and a device to protect against evil and witches. One theory was that iron represented Mars, who was the enemy of Saturn (god of witches) and a horseshoe was nailed to the door 'horns up' to make sure the luck did not run out of it, but to some a horse's shoe with its heels up is the unluckiest thing ever a man saw, particularly if it is travelling in his direction. In heraldry the shoe is often horns down and some say it is all that remains of the halo on the head of St Hubert (patron saint of hunting and hounds) which used to be painted or carved over stables. And because of its shape a horseshoe is symbolically linked with one of the most potent devices of all: the crescent, a universal symbol of fertility and prosperity.

LEGEND AND MYTH

The horse has such a strong grip on the human imagination that the list of mythological horses is endless. In Greek mythology, for example, Pegasus, the winged stallion, is so closely connected with poetic inspiration that it is hardly surprising there are so many imaginary horses in Greek stories.

GREEK MYTHOLOGY

In the Stone Age, primitive tribes on the Greek peninsula practised orgiastic horse-cult rituals which were probably the origin of the legend of the centaurs, those creatures that were half man, half horse, and which over the centuries have terrified races who have never seen ridden horses before. Though less bizarre than the centaurs, many Greek hero-horses had extraordinary powers, usually concerning swiftness and the ability to gallop through the air and over the waves.

PHOEBUS, the sun god, was drawn across the skies by a team of horses: ACTAEON (Effulgence), AETHON (Fiery Red), AMETHEA (No Loiterer), BRONTE (Thunder), ERYTHEROS (Red Producer), LAMPOS (Lamplight), PHLEGON (Burning Noon), PUROCIS (Fiery Hot).

PLUTO, god of the underworld, had horses too: ABASTER (Away from the Stars), ABATOS (Inaccessible), AETON (Swift Eagle), NONIUS.

AURORA, goddess of the dawn, was not to be outdone: ABRAXAS (Supreme Being), EOOS (Dawn), PHOETHON (Shining One).

ARION (Martial) was the first horse given to man. In one story it was born of the rape of the corn goddess, Demeter, by the sea god, Poseidon. Demeter attempted to escape Poseidon's lust by changing herself into a mare and mingling with the wild herds in Arcadia but Poseidon promptly turned himself into a stallion. In a less ungodly story, Arion was created when Poseidon brought it out of the earth by striking the ground with his trident.

Arion was a remarkable animal: it could speak, it had human feet, and its speed was legendary. Its first owner was Hercules (Heracles) but later it belonged to Adrastus. It was sacred to its progenitor, Poseidon, as were all Greek horses: they symbolized the crested waves ('white horses') and they drew the god's car over the ocean. They also flew.

PEGASUS is probably the best known of the many winged Greek horses. He sprang from the neck of the decapitated snake-tressed Medusa (she whose glance turned men to stone) when she was slain by Perseus. With a stamp of his hoof, Pegasus later created the Hippocrene spring on the mountain home of the Muses and one of his many roles was to fly poets into the realms of fantasy. Tamed by Bellerophon's golden bridle, Pegasus eventually retired to Olympia where his role was to fetch Zeus's thunderbolts.

HIPPODAMIA was the daughter of King Oinomaos of Pisa; her name meant 'tamer of steeds'. She was responsible for the world's first horse-race – a dangerous chariot race for those who sought to marry her. Prospective husbands raced against

Bellerophon on Pegasus. (Fotomas)

the king, who had winged horses, and the losers forfeited their lives. Young Pelops was given his own winged horse by Poseidon and also arranged for the king's chariot wheel to be loosened. The wheel duly fell off and the king was killed.

Very much later Zeus instructed Hercules to lay down strict rules for chariot-racing as a major event in the Olympic Games.

DIOMEDES won a splendid chariot race on the plains of Troy, arranged by Achilles and described in the *Iliad*. The heroic Diomedes was almost as brave as Achilles at the siege of Troy and his horses included DINOS the Marvel and LAMPON the Bright One. But there was another Diomedes, a tyrannical king of Thrace whose notorious carnivorous mares were fed on human flesh: he was eventually eaten by them himself, and the meal tamed them so that Hercules could complete his eighth labour. DIOMED was a real horse who won the first Epsom Derby in 1780. Presumably he was named in honour of the heroic Diomedes rather than the tyrant.

XANTHOS the Golden (the name means literally a reddish yellow) and BALIOS the Swift, according to Homer, were inherited by Achilles from his father Peleus, who had been given these immortal chariot horses by Poseidon. They had been sired by Zephyr the West Wind and their mother was the harpy Podarge the Swiftfooted. Xanthos was the first talking horse, granted the power of speech by Hera to warn Achilles of his imminent death but struck dumb again by the Furies.

THE TROJAN HORSE, as everyone knows and as Virgil relates, was a gigantic wooden con-trick, or 'military stratagem', in the siege of Troy. It was created by Ulysses after the death of Hector, ostensibly as an offering to the gods to ensure a safe voyage home. The huge wooden animal was accepted as a gift by the Trojans who dragged it into their city, unaware that a large number of Greek soldiers were hidden inside it.

There are countless other horses in Greek mythology, nearly always linked with heroes and kings. CERUS the Fit was the speedy mount of king Adrastus of Argos; Hector had horses like ETHON the Fiery, GALATHE the Creamy and PODARGE the Swiftfooted. Xerxes immolated a Thracian horse called STRYMON before invading Greece (he did other strange things, like sentencing the sea to 300 lashes for destroying his pontoon bridge). Horses are essential to the legends of Greece.

CELTIC LEGENDS

EPONA was originally a Celtic horse-goddess in Gaul, probably at first the deity of a spring (much like Pegasus) and worshipped as a spirited horse. Later, as a human goddess, she was always in the company of horses, usually riding a mare and feeding a foal. She was the protector of horses and mules, and was adopted by the Roman cavalry in the same role.

THE GREY OF MACHA was the chariot horse of the warrior Cuchulainn: the horse shed tears of blood when he was forced into the harness for what he knew would be the hero's final battle, and indeed the horse was mortally wounded by a spear which Cuchulainn drew out of The Grey's body though he himself was dying. The horse managed to rise and kick and bite the enemy as they closed in on his master.

EASTERN MYTHOLOGY

AL BORAK was the milk-white mare with the wings of an eagle and the face of a human who bore the Prophet Mohammed from earth to the seventh heaven: her name meant Lightning and she glittered all over. Her eyes were like jacinths and her every stride was as far as the human eye could see. At the horse's leaping off place as they ascended into the firmament, the second caliph, Omar al-Ka Hab, built a famous mosque.

KANTAKA was a white palfrey ridden by Gautama Buddha. In India, where in religion and art humans have great empathy with animals, the horse is a cosmic and solar emblem which represents sovereignty, the warrior aristocracy, prestige, victory, wealth and prosperity and it has a very special place in the Indian hierarchy of animals.

KUHAYLAH was a wild mare espied by Ishmael during a hunt: he thought the animal was an antelope and took aim but the angel Gabriel stopped him, saying that the mare was a beautiful gift from Allah and would become a great treasure to the Arabian people, whom Ishmael would father. When Kuhaylah foaled, Ishmael carried the new colt in his saddle-bag as he crossed the desert by camel but the jogging pace deformed the young animal's spine – and this, according to legend, is why many Arab horses have fewer vertebrae than other horses. Ishmael was prevented from destroying the colt by Gabriel (Jabrail) and in due course he was bred back to his mother and all Arabian horses were said to be descended from the pair.

RUKSH was the 'bright bay, with lofty crest' celebrated in Matthew Arnold's poem, *Sohrab and Rustum*. Sohrab was a Tartar warrior and his father, Rustum, was lord of the Persians against whom he fought. In the original Persian legend the horse was called Rakhsh and belonged to Rustam, whose brave exploits were recorded in the Book of Kings, *Shah-nameh*. The horse's lightning speed helped his master win many a battle and he was also credited with saving Rustam's life by killing a lion by biting it in the neck.

NORSE HORSES

ALSVID (All Swift) and ARVAK (Early Waker) were the Norse horses who drew the sun across the sky, pursued by the wolf Skoll. The gods gave them bellows under their yoke to keep them cool!

HRIMFAXI was driven across the skies by Nott, the swarthy goddess of the night. His frosty mane was dark and the rimy froth that fell from his bit became the early morning dew on the earth below.

SKINFAXI, in direct contrast to Hrimfaxi, had a shining mane and was driven across the skies by Nott's son, Dag, the god of the day, so that he could lighten the earth with his bright mane and tail.

SVADILFARI was an immensely powerful horse belonging to a giant who had taken on the task of constructing a protective wall around Asgard, the home of the gods. The contract terms demanded by the giant were that he should be given the sun, the moon and the goddess Freya if he managed to complete the work by the first day of summer. The great horse pulled stones as big as mountains and, with only three days to go before the summer deadline, the job was almost done. The god Loki rapidly changed himself into a mare and lured the big stallion away from his work. Thor, the god of thunder, killed the irate giant, and in the meantime Svadilfari and Loki produced their eight-legged offspring, SLEIPNIR, who could outrun the wind and cross land or water, and whose master was the one-eyed Odin (his other eye was the sun).

MEDIEVAL ROMANCES

BAVIECA was the horse of El Cid (Rodrigo Diaz de Bivar, who in real life died in 1099). The horse had at first belonged to the King of Seville but was won in battle by El Cid in the epic 12th-century poem, and he galloped so fast that he quickly became famous throughout Spain. Splendidly caparisoned, he became an inspiration on the battlefield and twice led the Christians as they put 50,000 Moors to flight. Bavieca's name meant 'simpleton', which was intended as a slur on El Cid rather than on the horse: one story relates that given the choice of a horse as a youth, he had picked the rough colt rather than a fully trained warhorse, and his godfather dubbed him a simpleton for doing so. Bavieca outlived El Cid by three years and was finally buried outside the gates of a monastery in Valencia, with two elm trees to mark his grave.

SHARATZ was the powerful piebald mount of the 14th-century Serbian king Marko Kraljevic, a legendary hero of epic poems. The horse could leap forward the length of four lances and upward the length of three, and in battle he would trample men to the ground, biting off their horses' ears for good measure!

BAJARDO, in Ariosto's *Orlando Furioso*, was a miraculous horse found by the wizard Malagigi. He was in a cave, guarded by a dragon which Malagigi had to slay. Bajardo was apparently immortal: Ariosto claimed that he lived forever but fled when anyone approached him, and no mortal could ever catch him.

CAROLINGIAN LEGENDS

BAYARD is the same name as BAJARDO or BAYARDO and is given to many valuable or wonderful horses, especially if they are bays. In Carolingian legend Bayard was a bright bay with a white star and he was owned by the four sons of Amyon: he could lengthen his back at will to accommodate them all in their adventures. He was also Rinaldo's horse, with an almost human intelligence, a fabulous speed, and a skin which could not be penetrated by any sword, but when Rinaldo first saw Bayard he was under a spell which made him fight viciously until he could be thrown to the ground to break the spell. Fortunately for Rinaldo, the horse caught his foot in some branches and fell so that he could immediately be gentled. But Rinaldo's faithful Bayard was stolen and sold to Charlemagne, who gave him to his own son, Charlot. Reclaimed by Rinaldo, the horse was promptly weighted with millstones by Charlot and thrown into a river: he resurfaced twice to struggle towards Rinaldo but the third time his master was ordered to stay out of sight and the horse, unable to see him, drowned. But it is said that the horse still gallops over the hills of the Ardennes on Midsummer Eve, and it is also said that his footprints can be seen in the forest of Soignes and on a rock near Dinant. And there are three stones known as Bayardo's Leap near Sleaford in Lincolnshire: they are thirty yards apart and the story is that the local demon leaped on Bayard's back behind Rinaldo but the horse took three gigantic leaps and shook off the intruder.

BEIFFROR (BROIEFORT) was a black Arabian won in battle by Ogier the Dane, who was seven feet tall and usually heavily weighted with armour. Only Beiffror was strong enough to carry him but eventually the horse was killed in Ogier's single combat with Bruhier the Saracen. Bruhier's mount was MARCHEVALLEE, and he kept a vial of magic balm under his saddle which healed all Bruhier's wounds during the fight, until Ogier chopped off his arm just as Beiffror was killed. Bruhier leapt off Marchevallee to retrieve his arm but was beheaded before he could reach his vial. Ogier commandeered Marchevallee and used the vial on his own wounds instead.

PAPILLON was the fire-breathing horse which carried the ship-wrecked Ogier across the Isle of Avalon to the magnificent palace of the fairy Morgana, where the enchanted Dane lived for a hundred years until the spell was inadvertently broken. Then Papillon took him to the island shores; sea-goblins carried them both across the sea and they sped to Paris, whence they helped to lift the Saracen siege of Chartres, with Papillon breathing fire on the enemy and Ogier wielding his magic sword.

RABICAN was a coal-black charger with a white star and great fleetness of foot. His sire was Wind, his dam was Fire, and he fed only on air. Like Bajardo, he lived in a cave guarded by a giant and a griffin, until he was claimed by Rinaldo.

WATER HORSES

Ever since Poseidon (or Neptune) created the horse, the animal has been associated with his domain: the sea and other waters. One of the many legends claims that Neptune created the horse during a contest with the goddess Minerva to claim the right to name Athens. Minerva (Athene) won because her creation, the olive tree, was adjudged more useful to the human race than the horse. But the god of the horses was widely worshipped in Europe, especially Greece and Italy, and in northern Africa, and in August there were many festivals in his honour in which horses were decked in flowers. They were also sacrificed to him, often by being driven over cliffs into the sea.

Poseidon and Neptune were not the only charioteers who could drive their horses over the waves: they had an Irish counterpart in Ler, whose son Manannan mac Ler was the patron saint of sailors and drove his chariot over the sea between Ireland and the Celtic Elysium: the white-capped waves are the White Horses of Manannan mac Ler, and his best horse was SPLENDID MANE.

In Scotland water-horses are known as KELPIES and they live in lochs and rivers. They are generally seen grazing innocently at the water's edge but if mounted they gallop into the water and the riders, magically glued to their backs, are drowned. Sometimes the kelpies appear as handsome young men to lure innocent maidens to their deaths. The BOOBRIE is another loch monster, sometimes taking the form of a water-horse.

The famous Rhine siren, the LORELEI, was finally carried away to her coral caves by white river horses drawing a sea-green chariot as huge waves swamped her shipwrecking rock home. In Norway a water-horse came to the rescue of those who lived by a fiord inhabited by a sea-serpent: during an ensuing fight the comb and front half of the serpent were washed ashore to form Front Comb Inlet, and the horse's severed hoof, found on the shore, was used as a 48-bushel corn-bin!

YEAR OF THE HORSE

The Chinese Year of the Horse falls between the Snake and the Goat. The Chinese new year is on the first new moon after the sun enters Aquarius (between 21 January and 19 February) and the Years of the Horse are:

1870, 1882, 1894, 1906, 1918, 1930, 1942, 1954, 1966, 1978, 1990

SCREEN STARS

In 1833 the horse was one of the sights to be seen on the 'wheel of life' zoetropes and praxinoscopes – children's toys in which rapidly repeated cartoon images gave an illusion of motion – but these were very rudimentary forerunners of the cinematographic moving pictures which, as it happens, were inspired by the horse.

People had argued for centuries about the sequence of a horse's leg movements in various gaits too fast for the human eye and in 1877 Governor Sandford of California made a $25,000 bet that, during the gallop, there was an instant when all four of a horse's hooves were off the ground simultaneously. To help him prove it, the Englishman Eadweard Muybridge set up an ingenious series of cameras to take chronological photographs of a horse in action: each camera was attached to a string which triggered the shutter when the horse touched it. Not surprisingly, the horse decided to jump the strings, and Muybridge therefore devised a mechanical system based on the type of cylinder found in music boxes which rotated to trigger the cameras in time with the horse's movements. The Governor won his bet, and cinematography was born when someone idly flicked through the series of photographs and found that the horse appeared to move. Today, films still work on the principle of flashing still pictures at a rate of two dozen frames per second so that we perceive motion.

RACING FILMS

The first motion picture of a horse race was of the 1895 Derby at Epsom, filmed by Birt Acres, and horse-racing has remained one of the most popular sports subjects in films, second only to boxing; the cumulative totals of sports films made from 1910 to 1987 show that 25% are based on boxing and 16.2% on horse-racing, though the number of films made each decade on the subject is dropping fast:

1910–1919
1 horse-racing film made

Muybridge's film experiment – the forerunner of today's cinema and inspired by a horse. (BFI)

1920–1929
32 horse-racing films made

1930–1939
41 horse-racing films made

1940–1949
21 horse-racing films made

1950–1959
11 horse-racing films made

1960–1969
5 horse-racing films made

1970–1979
3 horse-racing films made

1980–1987
1 horse-racing film made

The most famous and unlikely horse-racing film must be NATIONAL VELVET, based on Enid Bagnold's book (1935) in which a wall-eyed piebald gelding, part Arab and part cart-horse, with a phenomenal natural ability to jump, was won in a raffle by the 14-year-old Velvet Brown (played in the film by 12-year-old Elizabeth Taylor). Velvet gave her new horse a few try-outs at the local gymkhana and then rode him as a winner in the Grand National! In the film, The Piebald became a sorrel named KING CHARLES.

WESTERNS

Screen horses are not confined to racing. The first narrative film ever made was Andrew Porter's *The Great Train Robbery* in 1903, which set a fashion for the ubiquitous 'westerns' in which horses have always played a major part. Three years later the centre of American film production moved from the eastern states to California, where the locations were ideal for action-packed westerns, and as the horse became its rider's closest friend on celluloid, it also became popular as a star in its own right.

CHAMPION THE WONDER HORSE was Gene Autry's chestnut with a white blaze and four white stockings, appearing in films, on television and in Autry's touring shows. Autry's first film was *Tumbling Tumbleweeds* in 1935 and in eighteen years he starred in no less than 90 musical westerns. In the 1950s Champion was given his own television series, developed from a comic strip. The original Champion was in fact called Lindy (he was foaled on the day that Charles Lindbergh flew across the Atlantic) and his circus-like tricks included dancing, kneeling, untying knots and leaping through paper posters. Several other Champions followed during Autry's long career and they could dance the waltz, the rumba and the hula-hula.

DIABLO was the Cisco Kid's speckled roan, in company with Pancho's LOCO on television in the 1950s (the series began on radio in 1942). The original Cisco Kid was a Mexican bandit who rode around killing for pleasure, but long before the radio and television series he was turned into a romantic adventurer by several films.

FLICKA was the central character of a 1940s series of books by Mary O'Hara which soon became a series of Hollywood films, including *My Friend Flicka*. She was a wild filly on a Wyoming ranch, deemed to be 'loco' and untamable but chosen by a 10-year-old boy. On being captured she did indeed go loco, crashing her way through a barn window and nearly killing herself on a barbed-wire fence, but the boy's devoted care saved her and she became his friend.

FRITZ was one of the earliest cowboy personality horses: the pinto co-starred with Rio Jim (William Shakespeare Hart) in several movies, including *Pinto Ben*, from 1915 to 1925. The pair carried out all their own stunts including riding through plate-glass windows and leaping across overturned wagons. Fritz once saved Hart's life in reality during a night-shot sequence in

A still from My Friend Flicka. (BFI)

which they were swimming across a turbulent mountain stream. Fritz died at the age of 31 and was buried in Newhall, California, at Hart's Horseshoe Ranch which was opened to the public in 1958 as the William S. Hart Park.

PHANTOM was the white stallion of the *Zorro* television series of the late 1950s; there had earlier been two films (*The Mark of Zorro*, 1920 and 1940), and all were based on the Johnston McCulley novel, *The Curse of Capistrano*. They were set in Monterey in 1820 and centred around Diego Vega, an apparently idle Mexican aristocrat who led a secret life as the masked man in black galloping about on Phantom to avenge those who had suffered under the tyrannical Spanish governor of the colony. When Zorro was not riding Phantom, he was mounted on the black stallion TORNADO.

REX was the first horse to star in his own western. He was a black Morgan stallion who was the 'King of the Wild Horses' in the Hal Roach film *Black Cyclone* (1927). He did not need to act: he had been mistreated as a colt and was so unmanageable that a double was used for scenes with actors, but he was superb in action and one of his scenes involved an apparent fight with a mountain lion. He had been bought for $150 and over a 15-year starring career he earned a fortune for his owners.

SILVER will always be remembered from the cry, 'Hi-yo, Silver – Away!' His rider, the masked Lone Ranger, was created for a radio series in 1933, and this soon produced comic strips, books, films and a television series. In the first book (*The Lone Ranger*, 1938) Silver was a 6-year-old stallion who saved his herd from Sioux horse-hunters and was injured in a buffalo stampede, which enabled the Lone Ranger to capture him. Tonto, the Ranger's Indian companion (played on television by the Mohawk, Jay Silverheels), rode the pinto SCOUT.

TONY was Tom Mix's Wonder Horse in a film career beginning in 1917, and both man and horse were brilliant at stunts in their action-packed westerns. Mix was devoted to the sorrel horse with a blaze and two white socks, and made the film *Just Tony* (1922) as a tribute to him. They made more than sixty feature films for Fox (who later dedicated a huge studio to the pair) before they left in 1927 to tour with a circus. The horse was retired at the age of 23 in 1932 after a fall, and he died ten years later.

TOPPER was Hopalong Cassidy's snow-white horse. The original Cassidy was created in stories by Clarence E Mulford, but the character was completely taken over by William Boyd, who played the soft-spoken hero in 66 films between 1935 and 1948 and in a television series from 1948 to 1952.

TRIGGER was Roy Rogers' famous golden palomino, by a Thoroughbred out of a Quarter-horse mare. Bought by Rogers in 1938 for $2,500, Trigger appeared in more than a hundred films – including Rogers' tribute to him, *My Pal Trigger* (1946) – and then in the late 1950s came regular television appearances. Rogers dubbed Trigger the Smartest Horse in the Movies: he could walk 50 yd (46 m) on his hind legs, sit on chairs, untie knots, knock on doors, fire off guns, box, count to ten, sham a broken leg, pretend to fall down dead – and tuck his master into bed. Trigger died in 1965 and his stuffed body was put on display at the Roy Rogers & Dale Evans Museum in Victorville, California, alongside Dale's horse BUTTERMILK and the family dog.

MORE SCREEN HORSES

THE BLACK STALLION was a fabulous wild Arabian in Walter Farley's books, the first of which became a film in 1979. The wild creature was captured and forced to board a ship in a small Arabian port; the ship sank in a storm off Cape Finisterre and the only survivors were the horse and a young American boy who clung to his halter rope as the stallion swam to a small island. During their three-week marooning, the boy eventually gained the horse's trust. They were rescued and went home to Flushing, New York, where the boy rode the scarcely tamed horse in match races at Belmont.

FURY was another black stallion, the star of a television series in the 1950s which made him the second-highest animal earner in Hollywood (Lassie the collie was first). He was an American Saddlebred, foaled in Missouri and originally known as HIGHLAND DALE. In 1946 he appeared as BLACK BEAUTY in a film of Anna Sewell's much loved book, and then won acting awards from the American Humane Association for his performances in *Gypsy Colt* (1955), *Giant* (1957), and *Wild is the Wind* (1958). Yet in the 1960s he was found, starving and maltreated by a seedy cowboy, in a southern California animal park, whence he was rescued by Ralph and Toni Ringo Helfer and restored to health.

The **largest number of horses ever assembled for a film** was 11,000 in Alexander Ptushko's *Ilya Muromets* (*The Sword and the Dragon*), a Russian film made in 1956. In the same year **the Hollywood record** was set when King Vidor used 8,000 horses in *War and Peace*. One of the **most spectacular scenes** involving horses was in the 1959 film version of *Ben Hur*, in which four Lipizzaners jumped as a team over wrecked chariots in the famous chariot race: former stuntman Yakima Canutt directed the scene, stuntmen drove the nine chariots, and not one horse was injured.

HORSES IN LITERATURE

There have been countless horses in literature – they must be the most popular of all animals, especially as characters in their own right rather than simply as companions to humans (which is the usual role of the dog). They include the wild and unmanageable, the 'ornery', the heroic, the enduring, the fleet, the infuriating, the ludicrous and the comic, though a sense of humour is not always a strong feature of the literary horse. Here is a selection of them.

BLACK BEAUTY, Anna Sewell's classic story told from the point of view of the horse and published in 1877. The grandson of a Thoroughbred, Black Beauty was foaled on an English farm and began a pleasant enough life as a saddle and carriage horse, until a drunken rider galloped him over stones, with one shoe missing, so that he fell and injured his knees. Then he was sold successively until he became a London cab-horse, collapsing with the weight of an overladen cab when he was about 14 years old. His luck changed again: he was sold to three ladies who kept him in contented retirement. Although the story of

Black Beauty is unusual in being 'from the horse's mouth', it was not the first 'autobiography': in 1853 *The Field* serialized *The Life of a Racehorse* which contained splendid descriptions of stable lads and trainers of the time observed by a knowing horse.

BLACK BESS was Dick Turpin's mare in Harrison Ainsworth's *Rookwood* (1854). Though both the man and the horse did exist, their famous ride to York was pure legend: it was based on the ride of another highwayman, John Nevison, born in 1639, who staged a robbery near Rochester in 1676 and needed to establish a good alibi. He completed the long ride to York within 16 hours and was witnessed by the city's mayor playing bowls in the evening, but he used several horses, and his ploy failed to the extent that he was arrested and found guilty of the robbery, though he was subsequently pardoned by King Charles II, who admired his sporting feat. The real Richard Turpin, on the other hand, was a brutal man towards other men but adored his Black Bess – and other horses. He was caught stealing White Stockings, a race-horse, and accidentally shot his companion dead during the ensuing fight: he promptly disappeared but, rather than galloping Black Bess all the way to York overnight, he actually lay low for some time and then built himself a new persona as a Yorkshire country gentleman named Palmer. But he was arrested, and went to the gallows in 1739. No one knows what happened to the real Black Bess.

BREE and HWIN were talking horses in C S Lewis's *The Horse and his Boy* (1954). Bree taught the boy to ride so that he could return to Narnia, his birthplace, whence he had been stolen as a foal and trained as a warhorse by his captors. He was surprised to find that the

Narnians had too much respect for talking horses to ride them. HWIN was a talking mare in the same story; she carried the girl to Narnia.

THE BROGUE was the fairly useless brown gelding in Saki's *Beasts and Super-Beasts* (1914): he had 'personally created most of the gaps' in the hedges and banks for miles around as a hunter; as a hack he swerved at the sight of pigs, prams and white-painted gates, and on seeing a green gate which had previously been white he made a 'violent curtsey, a back-pedal, and swerve' when ridden by an unsuspecting rich new rider, who promptly gave the horse to his fiancée, whose family had been trying to sell The Brogue for years.

BRONZOMARTE was Sir Launcelot Greaves' mettlesome sorrel when he meandered around England trying to reform society and right wrongs in Smollett's *Adventures of Sir Launcelot Greaves* (18th century).

GARGANTUA'S MARE was as big as six elephants and her feet were cloven into toes. She was a burnt sorrel with dapple-grey spots, and her terrible tail was as tall as the tower of St Mars near Langeais. She used it so vigorously to switch at horseflies and hornets in a great forest near Orleans that she uprooted the trees. According to the Rabelais story (1535), the sight of her delighted Gargantua who exclaimed, 'Je trouve beau ce', and the area she devastated has been called Beauce ever since.

GRIZZLE was the pathetically skeletal old mare of Dr Syntax, the clergyman created by William Combe (1741–1823). The doctor's adventures were told in verse and illustrated by Rowlandson in colour cartoons. His first adventures were published in 1812 and he was pious, hen-pecked, simple-minded and optimistic, but had excellent taste

and scholarship. He was a firm believer in beauty lying in the eye of the beholder and preferred the bony old grey nag to 'the far-famed Eclipse'.

GUNPOWDER was the one-eyed, broken down old horse ridden by Ichabod Crane in Washington Irving's *The Legend of Sleepy Hollow* (1820) when he met a massive headless Hessian soldier on a powerful black horse. The Hessian hurled his head at Ichabod, who promptly fell to the ground and was never seen again, though the next morning Gunpowder was found calmly cropping grass near his master's hat and a shattered pumpkin.

THE HOUYHNHNMS were the intelligent horses who ruled the South Sea island where Gulliver was stranded during the fourth voyage of *Gulliver's Travels* (1727, Jonathan Swift). They were remarkably dexterous: they could thread a needle, milk a cow, make tools and pots, and harvest their crops, and they could concoct herbal medicines. They understood the solar year and held General Assemblies at the vernal equinox. Gulliver was able to converse with them in their own spoken language, and greatly admired their maxim 'to cultivate Reason, and to be wholly governed by it', and their virtues of friendship, benevolence, decency and civility – in sharp contrast to the inferior human race of Yahoos who worked as their servants and beasts of burden. Their name, which is Swift's approximation to the sound of a horse's whinnying, is pronounced 'whinims'.

THE PINK STALLION was the only unpublished work among the 1987 Betty Trask Award winners – and must surely be the first piece of romantic fiction to be written about cart-horses! The author, Lucy Pinney, is married to a horse-breeder and spent her honeymoon

Don Quixote with his trusted mare Rocinante. (Fotomas)

looking at cart-horses in the Ardennes.

ROCINANTE is perhaps the most memorable horse in literature: the 'extremely consumptive-looking' old stallion ridden by Cervantes' Don Quixote, usually dreadfully lethargic and scruffy but much loved by his knight. Rocinante would often drape his neck over that of Sancho Panza's ass, and the pair of them would stand there staring at the ground, for as much as three days on end.

CLAVILENO also appeared in the *Don Quixote* story (1616). This was a magic horse, said by the Distressed Duenna to have been created by Merlin and to be able to carry a rider through the skies without spilling one drop from a tumbler of water. It was a wooden horse with a peg in its neck to guide it (an idea borrowed from Chaucer's unfinished *Squire's Tale* in 1400, in which a wondrous brass steed had a peg in its ear). The knight and his friend Sancho were blindfolded and put astride Clavileno after dark: they

turned the peg and felt the air rushing past – because someone blew some bellows at them. Then the wooden horse's tail was lit, setting off rockets inside the horse and convincing its tumbling, dazed riders that they had sailed past the moon.

SILVER BLAZE was the central character in Conan Doyle's *The Adventure of Silver Blaze* (1892). He was a 5-year-old bay of Isonomy stock, favourite to win the Wessex Cup but he disappeared a week before the race and his trainer was found dead with a head injury. Sherlock Holmes solved the mystery in classic style, and the horse has been remembered since 1952 in the annual Silver Blaze Handicap at Belmont, attended by the Baker Street Irregulars.

STRIDER followed the tradition of the autobiographical horse in Tolstoy's *Strider: The Story of a Horse* (1886). The horse could not understand the concept of being someone's property: 'my horse' seemed as strange a phrase as 'my land', 'my air' or 'my water'. He was a piebald, sired by a Thoroughbred, and came to an end in the hands of the knacker, his carcass devoured by dogs and wolves. There was a musical based on the story in 1976 in Leningrad, which was adapted for a New York City production in 1979.

SHAKESPEARE

Horses whinny their way through many a Shakespearean play but most of them are anonymous steeds. There is a fine description of horsepower in *Venus and Adonis.*

CAPILET was the grey horse which Sir Andrew Aguecheek offered in appeasement to his rival, Sir Toby Belch, whom he had challenged for the rich countess Olivia in *Twelfth Night.*

CURTAL was the elderly Lord Lafeu's bay horse in *All's Well That Ends Well,* which he said he would gladly give, harness and all, to have the sound teeth and downy beard of youth.

CUT was a horse that the first Carrier in *Henry IV, Part I* asked the ostler to take care of at a Rochester inn: 'I prithee, Tom, beat Cut's saddle, put a few flocks in the point, poor jade is wrung in the withers, out of all cess.'

DOBBIN, quite apart from being a standard name for any old cart-horse, was Old Gobbo's horse in *The Merchant of Venice.* The old man was virtually blind and failed to recognize the son he sought in Venice. As Launcelot finally knelt for his father's blessing, he faced away from him and the old man declared: 'Thou hast got more hair on thy chin than Dobbin my fill-horse has on his tail.'

PETRUCHIO'S HORSE, who took his master to the wedding in *The Taming of the Shrew,* was 'possessed with the glanders and like to mose in the chine, troubled with the lampass, infected with the fashions, full of windgalls, sped with spavins, rayed with the yellows, past cure of the fives, stark spoiled with the staggers, begnawn with the bots, swayed in the back, and shoulder-shotten'.

THE ROAN BARBARY was Richard II's favourite, which Bolingbroke deliberately rode to his own coronation as Henry IV after Richard had been forced to abdicate and was imprisoned in Pomfret Castle. A groom reported that the horse had carried him proudly, and Richard exclaimed:

'So proud that Bolingbroke was on his back!
That jade hath eat bread from my royal hand;
This hand hath made him proud with clapping him.
Would he not stumble? would he not fall down,
Since pride must have a fall, and break the neck
Of that proud man that did usurp his back?
Forgiveness, horse! Why do I rail on thee,
Since thou, created to be awed by man,
Wast born to bear?'

But Harry had always been a good horseman:

'I saw young Harry, with his beaver on,
His cushes on his thighs, gallantly arm'd,
Rise from the ground like feather'd Mercury,
And vaulted with such ease into his seat,
As if an angel dropp'd down from the clouds,
To turn and wind a fiery Pegasus,
And witch the world with noble horsemanship.'

King Henry IV, Part I

WHITE SURREY was the horse saddled for Richard III's fated battle on Bosworth Field: the horse was slain during the fighting, and hence one of the most quoted phrases from Shakespeare: 'A horse! A horse! My kingdom for a horse!' He might well have echoed the cry, 'O, for a horse with wings!' in *Cymbeline*, or 'The man shall have his mare again, And all shall be well' in *A Midsummer Night's Dream*.

RHYMES

An old rhyme tells of the Norse god Odin's ride on BALDUR THE BEAUTIFUL, who slipped and broke his leg, which Odin immediately cured by tying a black thread in seven knots. The seven-knot cure persisted in Cornwall to heal poisoned thumbs.

'Baldur rade, the foal slade,
He lighted, and he righted,
Set joint to joint and bone to bone,
Sinew to sinew;
Heal in Odin's name.'

There was an old French military proverb, much used in the 17th century, that the loss of a nail meant the loss of an army, and this was developed into that cautionary rhyme:

'For the want of a nail the shoe was lost,
For the want of a shoe the horse was lost,
For the want of a horse the rider was lost,
For the want of a rider the message was lost,
For the want of a message the battle was lost,
For the want of a battle the kingdom was lost,
And all for the want of a nail.'

The annual fair at Widdecombe in Devon is probably so famous only because of the very popular song:

Tom Pearce, Tom Pearce, lend me your grey mare,
All along, down along, out along lee,
For I want for to go to Widdecombe Fair,
Wi' Bill Brewer, Jan Stewer, Peter Gurney, Peter Davy, Dan'l Whiddon, Harry Hawk, and old Uncle Tom Cobbley and all.'

That old grey mare took sick and died, not surprisingly, and:

'When the wind whistles cold on the moor of a night,
All along, down along, out along lee,
Tom Pearce's old mare doth appear, gashly white . . .
And all the long night be heard skirling and groans,
All along, down along, out along lee,
From Tom Pearce's old mare in her rattling bones . . .'

All the men in the song were real people, registered in the baptismal records of Crediton parish church.

Another famous rider in rhyme was the Banbury Cross lady:

'Ride a cock-horse to Banbury Cross,
To see a fine lady upon a white horse.
With rings on her fingers and bells on her toes,
She shall have music wherever she goes.'

The lady might well have lived in Tudor times, when toe-bells were fashionable, or she might have been the naked Lady Godiva (usually of Coventry) warning people of her approach by ringing a hand-bell and jangling other bells fastened to her stirrups. Another suggestion was made by someone living in South Africa whose family descended from the Norman line of Fiennes and had a tradition that a nobleman of the house of Fiennes married a darkly beautiful Spanish lady and took her to his castle near Banbury. She always rode a white horse, and no doubt a 'fine lady' could have been a 'Fiennes lady'. Perhaps her white horse was an Andalusian?

THE ENTERTAINERS

Quite apart from fiction, there have always been 'talking' horses and there have also been High Schools for horses to teach them rather different arts. But both the talkers and the *Haute École* dancers have found careers as entertainers of one kind or another.

"...and now let us discuss the intelligence of man..."

Prof. McHighland

HIGH SCHOOL HORSES

Haute École, or the art of dressage, derives from the days when horses were trained for war. At one time they were used not only to carry warriors but also as weapons, stamping, rearing, pawing the air, bounding high and lashing out with their hind feet or striking with their forefeet. Once the heavily encumbered knights on their destriers or chargers had been replaced by lightly armed cavaliers on faster horses, the need was for the horse to get its rider out of trouble in hand-to-hand mêlées, and the rears, leaps, pirouettes and lashing hind-legs all played their part. Eventually all these movements became part of an art for the sake of it rather than of practical value in battle.

In due course two main streams of classical equitation evolved: that based on the French Schools at Versailles and Saumur, and that of the Spanish Riding School in Vienna (it was called Spanish because of its use of Spanish horses and it was first built in 1572, then rebuilt in 1735). The Lipizzaners became and remained synonymous with the Spanish School in Vienna; the Saumur became the French Cavalry School which used Thoroughbreds.

CIRCUS

The *Haute École* rider remains virtually motionless in the seat, and in contrast the circus rider and trainer make a great display of body movements, cracking whips and general spectacular ostentation, but many of the teaching methods and movements are similar. In the circus the horses are often called Liberty Horses: they include Lipizzaners and showy Arabs but also more mundane breeds, though preferably horses rather than ponies, which are more independent and therefore more difficult to train. The whip, incidentally, is merely a 'guider' acting as an extension of the trainer's arm and showing the horse what to do next: it cracks the air, and does not touch the horse.

THE RUSSIAN HIPPODROME

In Russia in the 1950s, hippodromes were race-courses with training stables. For example, in Moscow 800 horses were stabled in well-made barns; each trainer was responsible for perhaps 50 horses. There was a team of jockeys and trotter drivers, and a groom for every four horses, as well as seven veterinary surgeons and a modern veterinary hospital on the site. The Moscow race-course was a floodlit one-mile circuit. Some of the state-controlled stud farms of the time were huge: a 'small' farm had perhaps 300 mares and a stallion, and a large one, or 'factory', might have 3,000 mares. The farms often covered many thousands of acres and were self-sufficient, growing their own food and often raising cattle as well as horses. A typical farm scene was 200 mares with their foals grazing on enormous open plains in the care of a couple of mounted herdsmen.

THE LONDON HIPPODROME

The London Hippodrome was no Russian race-course. It was constructed in 1851 (the year of the Great Exhibition) by William Batty, who found a piece of ground in Kensington, put up a wooden building capable of holding 14,000 spectators, and called it the Hippodrome (from the Greek for horse and course). He then engaged the famous Paris Hippodrome's men and horses, under their manager M Soullier, to present a programme of equestrian events including a ladies' steeplechase, a chariot race with the horses four abreast (the *quadriga*) and so on, many of the events copied from earlier circuses.

In 1887 the circus was best known by the name of 'Horsemanship' which had been unknown in England before the end of the 18th century though the Romans were said to have 'amused themselves with mimic chariot races in an arena' in southern England and there were the remains of amphitheatres near Dorchester, Banbury and St Albans.

But it was not until the 1760s that equestrian performances were re-introduced; and it was another twenty years or more before 'the acrobat and the wild beast tamer joined hands with the circus proprietor, and presented an entertainment resembling that now given at a circus' (*The Field*).

During the first half of the 19th century nearly all the historical

Marocco, Mr. Banks' 'educated' horse.

romantic operas included a scene in which a pair of horses performed on stage, and there was even a circus production of Shakespeare's *Richard III.*

William Batty's London Hippodrome of 1851 was subsequently turned into an outdoor riding school, and then came into the hands of Messrs Blackman; thereafter all the gates, fences and stables made way for Baron Grant's mansion, which had itself been supplanted by 1887. But the word Hippodrome has always had equine connections, whether as a chariot-racing course or as a circus. Only later did it come to be merely a variety theatre without a horse in sight.

EDUCATED HORSES

Much older than the circus is the 'educated horse', and here are some of them:

MAROCCO was a real Elizabethan horse, described by Shakespeare in *Love's Labour's Lost* as a dancing horse which could count, read dice and recognize colours. He was owned and taught by a Mr Banks and was famous not only in England but also in France, where the monks accused Banks of being a witch or a conjurer. He therefore asked one of them to hold up a crucifix: the horse knelt before it and the charge was dismissed. In 1600, they say, Marocco (also called Morocco) climbed to the top of the old St Paul's cathedral. He was a middle-sized bay gelding who came from Newmarket and Thomas Banks was a Scot. One of his dances was the Tudor jig, which he performed on his hind legs walking backwards in small circles while he remained upright.

BILLY was Sergeant Philip Astley's first purchase when he resigned from the 15th Light Dragoons in 1766 to open a riding school and give shows in a field near Westminster Bridge. Bought as a wedding gift for his bride, the pony was so trainable that he became Astley's favourite performer. He would take a kettle off the stove and set the tea table, for example. Two years later Astley developed his riding ring into a circus by bringing in acrobats, clowns, rope-walkers and two pipers to supplement his wife's drumming. His own riding acts included standing with one foot on each of two horses while they leaped over gates and fences and standing on his head on a trotting horse's saddle.

ALPHA was an educated horse who could add, subtract, pretend to be lame and, claimed his trainer Zucker, write in chalk on a blackboard at the beginning of the century, but he was excelled by de Kroutikoff's ANTAR, who could *read* from the blackboard by spelling out the chalked word with lettered blocks.

MERLIN was Lord Lonsdale's shooting-pony, son of one of the team of cream Hanoverians which drew the royal coach and which had been presented to Lonsdale by King George V. Merlin could dance, bow, jump, beg, pick up a handkerchief, lie down, roll over, and cross his legs – all on command. Lonsdale said that Merlin was in no way exceptional: all his thirty shooting-ponies would do the same – or so he told Bertram Mills.

KLUGE HANS, or CLEVER JACK, was a Russian stallion trained by Wilhelm von Osten, an elderly German in Berlin who bred horses as a hobby. Hans could count blackboard numbers by pawing the ground; he could add, subtract, divide and multiply. Vets, circus managers, cavalry officers and university professors could find no trickery in his act but the psychologist Oscar Pfungst said that the horse was prompted by barely perceptible body language from von Osten.

However, the old man's student Karl Krall taught several other horses the rudiments of arithmetic in a matter of days – and square and cube roots in months. They rarely made a mistake, indicating units with the left foot and tens with the right. They also learned the alphabet and could both 'read' and 'write' (by pawing). They gave intelligent answers to tricky questions and 'conversed' with visitors even when their master was absent.

Best of the bunch was MOHAMMED, who was said to be a brilliant and pithy conversationalist who spoke in German but with a mode of expression having something in common with written Arabic – all consonants and no vowels (for example, the German Pferd for horse was FRT; Zucker for sugar was ZKR) though he carefully spelled out vowels in proper names.

MR ED was a television talking horse in a 1961 series. The palomino could use his mouth to untie knots, wave a flag, write notes with an outsize pencil and other party tricks. When he 'talked', he actually had a halter with a nylon line running through his mouth: his trainer Les Hilton, out of sight, tugged the line to make the horse's lips move like those of a ventriloquist's dummy,* and the words were dubbed by an actor. The horse won the American Humane Association's Patsy award four times and died in 1979.

WORD POWER

SYNONYMS

In 1911 *Roget's Thesaurus* gave the following equine synonyms:

Arab	hunter
barb	jade
bayard	jennet
bidet	jument
blood horse	ketch
broncho	mare
bronco	mustang
cart-horse	nag
cattle	Narragansett
cayuse	pack-horse
charger	pad
cob	palfrey
colt	pony
courser	post-horse
cow pony	punch
creature	race-horse
crittur	racer
destrier	roadster
draft-horse	roan
dray-horse	sheltie
filly	stallion
foal	steed
galloway	stud
garran	thoroughbred
garron	tit
gelding	Waler
genet	war horse
goer	
hack	Bucephalus
hobby	Pegasus
	Rocinante

Foreign words for the horse given by Stonehenge in the 1860s:

ARABIC hozan
BORNOU fúr, pur
DANISH hest
DUTCH paard
FRENCH cheval
GERMAN pferd
GREEK hippos
ITALIAN cavallo
LATIN equus
POLISH kon
PUSTOO as

Alexander the Great with his renowned horse, Bucephalus.

RUSSIAN loschad
SIAMESE ma
SPANISH caballo
SWEDISH hast
SYRIAC hysan
TIMBUCTOO baree
TOORKMAN al
TURKISH sukh

HORSE WORDS

The word 'horse' used as an adjective to describe various plants and animals generally infers coarseness or large size. For example:

Horse bean (a broad bean)
Horse chestnut
Horse-foot (coltsfoot plant, or a king crab)
Horse-gowan (ox-eye daisy)
Horse-leech (a big leech; also a horse-doctor)
Horse mackerel (scad)
Horsemint (any wild mint)
Horse mushroom
Horse mussel
Horseradish
Horsetail or mare's-tail

The word is also used to denote coarseness in other objects and in people:

Horse-bread
Horse-faced
Horse-breaker (courtesan on horseback)

Horse-godmother (clumsy woman)
Horselaugh
Horse marine (someone out of their element)
Horse opera (a Wild West film)
Horse pistol (large pistol)
Horseplay

108

But the horse adjective is not always so rough:

Horse Latitudes (Atlantic region around 30° North and South where long calms are often encountered – the term is possibly connected with the sailing ships which carried horses to America and the West Indies and which would jettison part of the cargo when becalmed in these latitudes, since the horses needed plenty of drinking water)

Horse sense (good common sense)

Horse-trading (hard, shrewd bargaining)

Horseflesh ore (bornite or erubescite – the term 'horseflesh' described a reddish-brown colour)

As strong as a horse

To eat or work like a horse

Another implication of the word 'horse' is a supporting frame:

Horse or timber-mare (wooden frame on which soldiers used to be mounted as a punishment – it was a ridged oak beam, and the victim sat astride it with firelocks tied to both feet)

Horse (gymnastic apparatus for vaulting)

Clothes-horse

Saw-horse

worn-out subject, and the working of which is doing work which has already been paid for – such work is a dead horse because you cannot get any more out of it

Dobbin Steady horse, or a child's horse

Horse-and-foot Literally, cavalry and infantry – hence with all one's forces or might

A gift-horse Don't look a gift-horse in the mouth – i.e. don't inquire too deeply into the intrinsic value of a present

PHRASES AND
PROVERBS

A blind horse To whom a nod is as good as a wink

Horse-and-buggy Hopelessly out of date

A dark horse One whose abilities are unknown publicly

Cob of the county The boss – a cob is so-called because it is stout and big, but the word also means a tuft or head (cop) and therefore eminent, large, powerful

A rich cob A plutocrat

A dead horse The flogging of which is equated with trying to revive a

The grey mare Said to be the better horse – i.e. the woman rules her husband

The grey mare's tail A Scottish waterfall made by the stream issuing from Lochskene

A hobby-horse Originally a hobby was a small horse; then a hobby-horse was the draped wickerwork frame 'ridden' by Morris dancers and hence a child's toy horse consisting of a stick with a horse's head – there is still a Hobby Horse parade at Padstow in Cornwall on May Day

The high horse People of rank used to ride tall horses – hence being on one's high horse is to be arrogant and overbearing

Horse and hattock! Signal by witches or fairies to mount and flee

The iron horse Steam locomotive

Mare's nest A great discovery which proves to be nothing of the kind – also, in Devon, a *blind mare's nest*, which means nonsense

The horse's mouth Straight from which is direct from the highest source – the only sure way of knowing a horse's age is by examining its teeth

Nightmare The incubus – nothing to do with horses but an evil spirit personifying the type of dream in which there is pressure on the chest and inability to move – the demon was also supposed to rape sleeping women; *'away the mare'* means farewell to the blues, the mare being the nightmare

O'Donohue's white horses Foam-crested waves on a windy day – the hero O'Donohue is said to reappear every seventh year on May Day, gliding over the lakes of Killarney on his white horse, preceded by flower-strewing fairies and accompanied by sweet, unearthly music

The Pale Horse Death – one of the horses ridden by the Four Horsemen of the Apocalypse in the Revelations of St John the Divine was pale, the others being white, red and black: two were agents of war and two of famine and pestilence

Podunk A 'one-horse town' – after the American Indian name for a place near Hartford, Connecticut

Pony £25, or a small beer-glass holding less than a gill, or a person on the right of a card dealer

Shanks's mare or pony Your own shanks, i.e. legs

The ten-toed horse To walk on your own feet

The two-legged mare The gallows

To win the horse or lose the saddle Double or quits: a man once made a bet, with a horse as the stake, that another could not recite the Lord's Prayer without being distracted, and halfway through his recital the accepter of the bet said, 'By the by, do you mean the saddle as well?'

To win hands down To win easily – a jockey who is winning comfortably rides with hands down

White horses White-capped waves

The wooden horse Apart from the Trojan and Clavileno – a ship

The phrase *to put the cart before the horse* (i.e. reverse the natural order of things) is found in many languages, though most of them refer to oxen rather than horses.

There are many more horse proverbs. For example:

You can take a horse to water but you can't make him drink.

Don't change horses in midstream.

A good horse cannot be of a bad colour.

There is nothing so good for the inside of a man as the outside of a horse.

If you can't ride two horses at once, you shouldn't be in the circus.

A short horse is soon curried.

It's too late to shut the stable-door after the horse has bolted.

Three things are not to be trusted: a cow's horn, a dog's tooth and a horse's hoof.

If two ride on a horse, one of them must ride behind.

If wishes were horses, beggars would ride.

Set a beggar on horseback and he'll ride to the Devil.

There is nothing so bold as a blind mare.

He who has seen tree-tops bend before the wind or a horse move knows all there is to be known of the art of dancing.

Gypsy gold does not chink and

glitter; it gleams in the sunlight and neighs in the dark.

WHO SAID THAT?

'If he were a horse, nobody would buy him; with that eye no one could answer for his temper.' Walter Bagehot, speaking of Lord Brougham's glare

'The tigers of wrath are wiser than the horses of instruction.' William Blake

'Boot, saddle, to horse, and away!' Robert Browning

'I don't mind where people make love, so long as they don't do it in the street and frighten the horses.' Mrs Patrick Campbell

'To God I speak Spanish, to women Italian, to men French, and to my horse German.' Emperor Charles V

'England is the paradise of women, the purgatory of men, and the hell of horses.' John Florio

'A generous creature a horse is, sensible in some sort of honour, and made most handsome by that which deforms men most – pride.' Thomas Fuller

'Men are not hanged for stealing horses, but that horses may not be stolen.' George Savile, Marquis of Halifax

'I will drive a coach and six horses through the Act of Settlement.' Sir Stephen Rice

'Go anywhere in England where there are natural, wholesome, contented, and really nice English people; and what do you always find? That the stables are the real centre of the household.' George Bernard Shaw

'The best carriage horses are those which can most steadily hold back against the coach as it trundles down the hill.' Anthony Trollope, referring to political parties

'Do not trust the horse, Trojans. Whatever it is, I fear the Greeks even when they bring gifts.' Virgil

'Under bare Ben Bulben's head,
In Drumcliff churchyard Yeats is
  laid . . .
On limestone quarried near the spot
By his command these words are
  cut:
  Cast a cold eye
  On life, on death.
  Horseman, pass by!'
                                    W B Yeats

HORSE PLACES

HORSEBRIDGE, hamlet on the Tamar above Gunnislake (pack-horse, riding or bridle bridge)

HORSE EYE, Sussex (horse island)

HORSEHEATH, Cambridge (heath where horses are kept)

111

HORSELL, Surrey (shelter for animals in a muddy place)

HORSENDEN, Bucks (hill where horses are kept – likewise HORSENDON HILL, Middlesex)

HORSEPATH, Oxford (horse path)

HORSEY, Norfolk (horse island)

HORSEY PIGNES, Somerset (horse island – Pignes being another place nearby)

HORSFORD, Norfolk (horse ford)

HORSFORTH, Yorkshire (horse ford)

HORSHAM, Sussex (ham or meadow where horses are kept)

HORSHAM ST FAITH, Norfolk

HORSINGTON, Somerset (the town of Horsa's people)

HORSLEY (pasture for horses)

HORSMONDEN, Kent (horsekeepers' pasture)

HORSTEAD, Norfolk (horse farm)

HORSTED, Kent (horse farm)

HORSTED KEYNES, Sussex (horse farm belonging to Wills de Cahainges, 1068)

MARDEN, Kent (pasture for mares)

MAREFIELD and MARESFIELD are *not* horse names – the MAR or MARE suffix usually means marsh, marten, boundary, lake, sea etc.)

STEDHAM, Sussex (ham where the stallions graze)

THE NAME GAME

The naming of a horse demands more than mere imagination, and the standard expression that a horse is 'by' its sire and 'out of' its dam can lend an extra dimension of wit to the whole business.

ARK ROYAL's offspring have names like EAGLE, HERMES and OCEAN – which are all Royal Navy aircraft carriers.

PETOSKI, BUSTINO, BOLDBOY

and HAMETUS share two things in common: they are all Lady Beaverbrook's horses and, traditionally, their names have seven letters. (EASTER SUN was an exception, because he was foaled on Easter Sunday.)

ALDANITI (breeder Tommy Barron's grandchildren were AListair, DAvid, NIcola and TImothy).

KYBO and SIR KYBO reminded owner Isidore Kerman of his childhood: his mother would put the initials KYBO at the end of every letter (Keep Your Bowels Open).

LLAMEDOS is not a Welsh name. Read it backwards.

Here are some 'by . . . out of' names, and the more modern they are the less subtle they seem to become:

PALL MALL, by PALESTINE out of MALAPERT

FLIPPER, by WINDSOR SLIPPER out of FLAPPER

WAVERING BEE, by WAVETOP out of FLYING BEE

LOVE-IN-IDLENESS, by LONE ROMANCE . . .

HAPPY KNIGHT, by COLOMBO out of HAPPY MORN

SUN STORM, by SOLARIO out of TORNADO

CLEAVAGE, by HILLANDALE out of DIVIDED

ABDUL THE BUL BUL, by GIGANTIC out of TURKISH DELIGHT

IAGO, by DON JOHN out of SCANDAL

BUCKTHORN, by VENISON out of LELIA

PUNCH, by PARADOX out of MARIONETTE

THE ROUE, by CLARET out of ROULETTE

SORROW, by DEFENCE out of TEARS

A–Z–U: ASSES TO ZEBRAS TO UNICORNS

DOMESTIC ASSES (donkeys) are descended from the wild African ass.

MULES and HINNIES are hybrids achieved by crossing asses with horses: a mule's parents are a jackass and a mare, while a hinny's are a stallion and a jenny.

ONAGERS and HEMIONES are the wild asses of Asia, and they range from a light-coloured, swift-footed onager standing about 12 hh to the big 14 hh kiang of the Tibetan plateau.

ZEBRAS are now of three species; a fourth, the quagga, was exterminated in the 1880s.

ASSES

The ass (the word donkey has only been used since the late 18th century) is the only domesticated animal from the African continent apart from perhaps the cat. It was a very early domesticant: the Egyptians probably bred asses in captivity by the fourth millennium BC, long before anybody tamed the horse, and by the 5th Dynasty (2500–2345 BC) domesticated asses were often shown in Egyptian art– for example on the Beni Hasan tomb–usually as pack animals. They were certainly in western Asia early in the third millennium BC. Their wild ancestor, the African ass, was restricted to northern Africa in modern times but might possibly have evolved in Asia, which is the home of the onagers.

However, the domestic ass of Asia does not produce fertile offspring when crossed with an onager, but it does produce fertile offspring when crossed with either a European donkey or an African wild ass– which suggests that it originated from the African ass, not the Asian onager or hemione.

Asses came to Britain with the Romans. They were very popular by the 16th century, when horses became cannon fodder and were therefore scarce, and by the 19th century donkeys were quite common on farms and as town pack animals at a time when Welsh donkeys were fetching high prices. They were always popular in Ireland, where they generally carried goods such as peat, potatoes and flax, but were never common in Scotland. The donkey has always been the poor man's friend, being cheap to keep on common grazing, but white asses were often owned by royalty and the nobility.

DONKEYWORK

Donkeys have performed all kinds of jobs. They have carried large ladies to 'take the waters' at spas as well as holiday children at the seaside; they have been ridden by miners on their way to the colliery as well as working underground; they have pulled lawn-mowers, dust-carts, laundry-wagons, costermongers' vans, family traps and milk-carts–and they have also been milked, not only by Cleopatra for her bath. There used to be a herd of milch asses in London milked on the doorstep to supply a fresh drink for the children of wealthy customers, and in other parts of the world ass's milk has been used medicinally and cosmetically. In some parts their dung has been used as a medicant and is said also to make the best possible manure for pomegranates. Their skin has been converted into parchment and leather. In South America people eat smoked donkey meat.

When horses ceased to be cannon fodder, their numbers at home increased to the detriment of the donkey. Then came the internal combustion engine, which put the working horse out of a job and almost eradicated the donkey: the numbers were down to three figures in the 1930s in Britain, and they stayed low until the early 1960s when they found new roles as pets. Today they are in the show-ring and in the paddock; they are ridden and driven; they act as companions to lonely horses; and, with their patience, predictability and intelligence, they are invaluable in helping physically and mentally disabled children. There are now perhaps 1600 donkeys in this country and their average lifespan is a very healthy 37 years. In stark contrast, up to 4,000 feral donkeys are shot every week in Australia, where they are considered to be pests. Most of the species of wild African ass are now extinct.

ASS BREEDS

About seventy ass breeds are listed in Mason's *World Dictionary of Livestock Breeds* in 1988, and another dozen are extinct or nearly so. Some interesting breeds are:

BENDERI of southern Iran: originated from onager crossed with Iranian ass

CANINDE of Brazil: a rare variety, black with pale belly

DAMASCUS: usually brown to black but can be white

HAMADAN of Iran and Turkmenistan: usually white

HASSAWI: white Egyptian

JINNAN of the Yuncheng basin in China: black, often with white on nose and around eyes and on belly

NORTHEASTERN of Brazil: colours can be grey, agouti or purple-brown

PEGA of Brazil: roan or dark grey, of Italian and Egyptian origin, also called the Lagoa Dourada; the name Pega means 'manacles', the brand of the original breeder, J de Resende of Lagoa Dourada

POITOU of western France: long black or brown hair; nearly extinct

SIUMI of Shaanxi, China: large

with dark coat and paler muzzle and underparts, also called Four-eyebrows or Swallow-coat

SPOTTED of USA: America's Appaloosa ass

DONKEY LORE

The characteristic 'cross' on the donkey's back is a combination of the typical dark dorsal stripe seen along the back of many wild and primitive horses, with a horizontal band across the shoulders. With the donkey's biblical connections, especially that it carried Jesus on the first Palm Sunday, the hairs of this cross were believed to have healing powers.

For example, in the case of whooping cough, you took some of the cross's hairs and either put them in a flannel pouch hung round your neck or chopped them finely and mixed them with butter to fill a bread sandwich. In Yorkshire, Sussex and other parts of the country – and not so long ago – three hairs plucked from the cross were believed to protect a child from measles: the hairs were put in a bag around the child's neck and it then

mounted the donkey, facing backwards, to follow a special route nine times in order to seal the charm.

As a charm against being struck by the hand of god, a Mesopotamian child would wear about its neck a tuft of wool enclosing a pretty unpleasant mixture of pig manure and the excrement of a black dog mixed with ass's saliva. Another prescription of that period to protect children from the child-killing she-demon Lamasthu included seven red threads, hair from the right-hand side of a jack-ass's beard, hair from the left-hand side of a she-ass's beard, hair from the mane of an ass's colt and a tuft of black hairs pulled from the right side of an ass's rump – with a white pig's bristle for good measure!

Here is more donkey lore, some of it true:

If a donkey brays incessantly and keeps twitching its ears, rain is on the way.

Donkeys anticipate their own deaths and hide themselves away before dying. If you chance across a dead donkey, which is more rare than a four-leaf clover, good luck is coming to you.

Donkeys bring luck to herds of cattle if allowed to run with them at pasture – and they also eat plants which would otherwise be harmful to the cattle or would taint the cows' milk.

Donkeys have minds of their own: they can be willing and obedient but only in their own time and at their own pace.

Asses were generally used as pack animals in ancient times. The Jews and Nubians were probably the first to ride she-asses.

Roman newly-weds regarded the ass as a symbol of sexual potency.

An Egyptian ass-god was crucified in the 3rd century AD. Egyptians were always proud of white asses.

The Sultans of Muscat used large, graceful asses as their processional mounts until quite recently.

The ass was sacred to the corn goddess, Ceres.

According to Pliny, 60,000 sesterces was the price of a Sabinian ass from Reate, a province as renowned as the Greek Arcadia for its fine asses.

According to Varro, 400,000 sesterces was the price paid by Senator Q Axius for two pairs of draught asses.

King Midas, he of the golden touch, was said to have had ass's ears. Apollo and Pan asked Midas to decide which of them was the better musician; Midas chose Pan and Apollo disgustedly changed his ears into those of an ass. The Phrygian king hid the ears under his Phrygian cap but his barber discovered them. (There was a king called Portzmach in Brittany who had horse's ears and had all the barbers in the kingdom put to death in case they should discover his secret.)

In 260 BC there was a Consul called Cornelius Scipio Asina because of his big ears.

FAMOUS ASSES

ABDUL was a Greek burro used by James Simpson Kirkpatrick, an Australian stretcher-bearer, to carry the wounded after the Gallipoli disaster in 1915. Day after day little Abdul toiled down the dangerous 'Shrapnel Gully' with soldiers on his back, taking them to the aid station, even after Kirkpatrick was killed. A statue of Abdul, with an Anzac on his back, was put in the Shrine of Remembrance at Melbourne, and in 1964 the statue was reproduced on postage stamps commemorating the 50th anniversary of the Gallipoli landing.

ALIBORON appeared in La Fontaine's fable *The Thieves and the Ass*: while two thieves argued over Aliboron, a third stole him, and when the three fought about the ass a fourth stole him.

BALAAM'S ASS was the talking donkey in the Old Testament (Numbers 22:21–35) who was carrying the Midianite seer to meet the Moabite king, Balak, who wanted Balaam to curse the children of Israel. The Angel of the Lord, armed with a sword to slay Balaam but visible only to his ass, blocked their path and the animal turned aside. Balaam hit her but she turned again, wedging his foot against the wall. He hit her again and she lay down, so he hit her a third time and the Lord gave her the power of speech: 'What have I done to you that you have struck me these three times?' Balaam said she was making a fool of him, and she continued: 'Am I not your ass on which you have ridden all your life long to this day? Was I ever accustomed to do so to you?' At last the angel became visible to Balaam and explained that the donkey had been trying to save his life.

Titania. Out of this wood do not desire to go:
Thou shalt remain here, whether thou wilt or no.
I am a spirit of no common rate.

Act III.   Scene I.

Bottom and Titania from Shakespeare's A Midsummer Night's Dream *by H. C. Selous* *c.1864.* (Birmingham Library)

BENJAMIN was the old donkey in Orwell's *Animal Farm* who took little notice of the rebellion and disputes, merely remarking that 'donkeys live a long time'. And he did, becoming increasingly gloomy and taciturn over the years.

BORONALI was an artistic donkey whose painting, *Sunset over the Adriatic*, was exhibited in Paris and well received by those who presumed the artist to be human. Some of the Montmartre set had tied a brush to the donkey's tail. The name Boronali, signed on the canvas, was an anagram of ALIBORON, and perhaps the animal had something to do with the child's game of pinning the tail on the donkey!

BOTTOM THE WEAVER was Shakespeare's ignorant, self-important mock hero in *A Midsummer Night's Dream* who had an ass's head and was caressed by Titania, the enchanted queen of the fairies.

BOUDEWIN or BALDWIN was an ass owned by a rich man in the 12th-century beast epic, *Reynard the Fox*. He worked hard and ate nettles and thistles, while the rich man's dog played with his master and was fed bones and meat from the table. Wanting similar affection, Boudewin jumped doglike to place his forefeet on his master's shoulders and kiss him on the face, for which he was beaten and sent back to his thistles. An ass is an ass.

BRIGHTY was a little feral burro in the Grand Canyon area for thirty years. Known as the Hermit of Bright Angel Creek, he was an independent creature: he was friendly but would struggle free if caught. While a suspension bridge was being built over the Colorado River, Brighty willingly acted as a pack animal and was rewarded with the honour of being the first to cross the completed bridge. He then hauled water for the National Park Service for six years until he was killed and eaten by two fugitives. The burro was immortalized in a book by Marguerite Henry, which was made into a film, and a bronze statue of Brighty was put in the visitors' centre in the canyon – but it was removed in 1980 and replaced by an exhibition which described the damage done locally by the thriving population of feral donkeys.

BURIDAN'S ASS is the character in a 14th-century allegory attributed to the French philosopher Jean Buridan. The ass is dying of hunger, with two equal bundles of hay equidistant from him: the dilemma is to choose between two equally valid alternatives. (Actually the ass was a dog: Buridan considered the basis upon which a dog makes choices and decided it was random.)

EEYORE was the old grey donkey in *Winnie the Pooh* (1926) who was the eternal gloomy pessimist.

THE GOLDEN ASS was the alternative title of the 2nd-century satirical romance *Metamorphoses* by Apuleius: it was the story of a young man accidentally changed into an ass and the trials that beset him before he regained his human form.

MODESTINE was the donkey which Robert Louis Stevenson bought for 65 francs and a glass of brandy to carry his gear on his tour southwards from Le Monastier, recorded in *Travels with a Donkey*. She was 'a diminutive she-ass, not much bigger than a dog, the colour of a mouse, with a kindly eye and a determined under-jaw': she was stupid, patient and friendly but 'her faults were those of her race and sex' and RLS found her exasperating – though he missed her sorely when he had sold her.

PLATERO (Spanish for 'silversmith') was an amiable little grey donkey who liked mandarin oranges, listened to the musings of his master, the Spanish poet Juan Ramon Jiminez, and leaned over his shoulder while he read poetry and wrote *Platero y yo*.

PUZZLE was a silly, gentle donkey who obligingly allowed himself to be covered in a lion's skin and exhibited as the Great Lion of Narnia in C S Lewis's *The Last Battle* (1956).

SANCHO PANZA'S ASS was the companion of Don Quixote's tired old jade, Rocinante.

ROYAL GIFT was a jackass given to George Washington by King Charles III of Spain in 1785. The 15 hh grey Catalonian was the first jackass to sire a mule in the United States: the gift had been made because Washington wanted to breed draught animals at Mount Vernon. The Marquis de Lafayette then contributed the black jackass KNIGHT OF MALTA, and jennets were sent over from Spain as well. Washington became the first breeder of American mules and also the first breeder of American jackasses.

SYMBOLIC ASSES

Whatever its qualities, the ass can never be a symbol of power, speed and beauty like the horse: it is too affable to be admired in that way. It is rarely seen in heraldry, for example, except where a pun is intended for families like Askew and Assil. And although it has for centuries been essential to mankind as a beast of burden, it is rarely boasted on a nation's arms or flags. For example, the donkey and the alligator represent Jamaica but only the alligator, or crocodile, is given a place in the Jamaican coat of arms.

MESOPOTAMIAN ARMS

It was not always thus. The Mesopotamians adopted several animals as religious symbols and

also used animals in their literature to convey a sense of character of the species. The ass was held in particularly high regard: before the horse was domesticated, it was the ass which was the mount of kings and famous men, and even when the horse did arrive it was considered incompatible with the dignity of monarchs.

There is a text from the 3rd millennium BC putting the ass in its rightful place: Gudea, the governor of the city of Lagash, tells of a dream in which a god instructs him to build a temple, and in the dream there was an ass at the right hand of the god. The goddess who interpreted the dream explained that the ass was Gudea, the loyal and faithful servant of the god. (It is pure chance that 'ass' is echoed in 'Assyrian' and in the names of some Assyrian kings such as Assurnirari . . .)

The Mesopotamian or Assyrian ass was a musician: it is commonly depicted seated and playing a harp. For example, on a plaque from the front of a harp found in the Royal Tombs of Ur (first half of the 3rd millennium BC) a seated ass plays the harp for a dancing bear while a smaller one shakes a sistrum, and elsewhere a donkey played the harp before a seated lion. The same harp-playing ass appears on the capitals of Roman columns.

DEMOCRATIC DONKEY

In the United States of America, on 15 January 1870, the cartoonist Thomas Nast drew a jackass labelled 'Copperhead Papers' as a symbol of the Democrats in *Harper's Weekly*. Two years later he drew Horace Greeley offering himself as the combined Democratic/ Republican presidential candidate with a donkey in the background being yoked by a Republican ox, and after Greeley lost his bid Nast drew a bucking donkey throwing

The Democratic Donkey.

him off its back. In 1879 the donkey was partnered for the first time with an elephant, and both these animals remain symbolic of their parties today.

ASININE WORDS

Asinine words in the 1911 *Roget's Thesaurus* included:

Ass
Burro
Caddy
Donkey
Hinny
Jackass
Ladino
Mule
Sumpter

The word DONKEY was first used in the late 18th century, when it was pronounced to rhyme with monkey–probably as a diminutive of 'dun' in reference to its colour, or from the name Duncan. It has also been called DICKEY, especially in East Anglia where it was known as DICKASS or DICKY-ASS (a term of endearment also found in 'dickey-bird'), or DICKY (diminutive of Richard), and NEDDY (diminutive of Edward). CUDDY is an abbreviation of Cuthbert and was commonly used as a donkey name in Scotland and the north of England. JACK simply denotes a male animal: it applies to several other species from owls, curlews and snipe to pike, rats, hares, rabbits and foxes. MIKE and MOKE are other donkey names. (And there is a genus of woodlice called Oniscus, which means 'little ass', the Greek for ass being *onos*.)

There are not many place-names referring to donkeys – the syllable 'ass' usually refers to ash-trees rather than asses, but ASSENDON in Oxfordshire is 'the valley of the ass', and there is a place called DONKEY TOWN in Surrey. There is a possibility that the personal name MUL might have been a nickname meaning mule: it is found in place-names like MOULSECOOMBE, MOULSFORD, MOULSHAM, MOULTON and MOULSOE.

ASININE PHRASES

AN ASS IN A LION'S SKIN A hectoring coward, or a fool pretending to be wise – from the fable of an ass which dressed itself in a lion's skin but was betrayed by its braying.

AN ASS WITH TWO PANNIERS A man walking with a lady on each arm.

THE ASS WAGGETH HIS EARS Those who lack learning but talk as if they were wise – indirectly from the Midas fable in which the king chose the music of Pan as better than that of Apollo: the 'ass is deaf to music' but still waggles his ears as if he appreciated it.

HONEY IS NOT FOR THE ASS'S MOUTH Persuasion will not persuade fools; gentle words will not divert unreasonable anger.

WRANGLE FOR AN ASS'S SHADOW Contend about trifles. In the Demosthenes story, a man hired an ass to go to Megara. In the heat of the midday sun he dismounted and sat in the ass's shadow to cool himself. The animal's owner complained that he had hired the ass, not its shadow, and the man had no right to sit there. While they squabbled about the matter, the ass made off and left them both in the glare of the sun.

THE ASSES THAT CARRY THE MYSTERIES (*asini portant mysteria*) The Roman clergy – an allusion to the custom of using asses to carry sacred symbols in procession.

ASSES' BRIDGE (*pons asinorum*) Impassable barrier to further progress – refers to the fifth proposition in the first book of Euclid, which was the first difficult theorem and which dunces rarely got over without help.

DONKEY'S BREAKFAST Straw-filled mattress in the merchant navy.

NOT FOR DONKEY'S YEARS Not for a very long time – an allusion to the tradition that you never see a dead donkey, but also a play on the animal's long ears.

THE DONKEY MEANS ONE THING AND THE DRIVER ANOTHER Different people see things from different points of view. In a Phaedrus fable, a donkey driver tries to make his donkey flee because the enemy is approaching. The donkey asks if the enemy will give him a double pack-saddle and, being told they will not, declares: 'Then what care I whether you are my master or some other?'

TO RIDE THE BLACK DONKEY To be obstinate.

TO TALK THE HIND LEG OFF A DONKEY To talk incessantly.

TWO MORE, AND UP GOES THE DONKEY A showman's cry at the fair – he promises that as soon as enough money is collected from the onlookers his donkey will climb a pole or ladder, but he always asks for 'two more pennies' and the trick is never performed.

WHO STOLE THE DONKEY? A snide dig at the police, referring to their inability to find a donkey thief in the force's early days. The correct answer is, 'The man with the white hat': white hats were made from the skins of donkeys, which were often stolen for sale to hatters.

DONKEY WORK Drudgery.

DONKEY ENGINE Small auxiliary engines or pumps playing a subsidiary role, in the same way as the donkey does less important work than the horse.

DONKEY JACKET Strong jacket with leather shoulders and patch pockets.

NODDING DONKEY Oil-well pump.

DONKEY QUOTATIONS

'With monstrous head and sickening cry
*   And ears like errant wings,*
The devil's walking parody
*   On all four-footed things.*
Fools! For I also had my hour . . .'

G K Chesterton

'The donkey is not a degenerate horse; he is neither a stranger, nor an intruder, nor a cross . . . His blood is pure, and although his nobility is less illustrious, it is just as worthy and good as the horse's. Why is there then so much contempt for this animal that is so good, so patient, so sober and so useful? Do men despise, even in animals, those that serve them too well and at little cost?'

Comte de Buffon

'The ass endures the load, but not the overload.'

Cervantes, *Don Quixote*

'She might have looked like a toy on castors, but there was good solid donkey under that winsome exterior. She wouldn't be led . . . People who believe you can move a donkey by dangling a carrot in front of its nose are quite wrong.'

Doreen Tovey, *Donkey Work*

MULERY

The mule, though defamed like donkeys for being stubborn, has a greater versatility than the ass by virtue of being a hybrid. These ass/horse offspring are infertile: you cannot breed two mules to produce another mule, or two hinnies to produce another hinny, but must always start afresh by mating an ass and a horse.

HIS FATHER'S EARS

A mule, which is a cross between a jackass and a mare, has a donkey-like front half – heavy head, large ears, neat front legs – and a horse-like rear end with stronger hind limbs and a tail which has long hair either from the root or for most of its length. By contrast a hinny, which is a cross between a stallion and a jenny ass, has a lighter head; its ears are shorter and more horse-like, and its tail, like a donkey's, is tufted.

The body size of the hybrid is larger than that of an ass and can also be larger than that of a horse. It exhibits a high degree of hybrid vigour, especially the mule, which has greater stamina, endurance, surefootedness and strength as a pack animal than either a horse or an ass.

MAMMOTH MULES

Mules can be bred in sizes to suit the breeder's purpose and some of them can be huge. The Poitevin, a dun French cart-horse with large feet suited to working on the region's marshy lands, is said to have such a limited mental capacity and so many defects in conformation that it is fairly useless as a work-horse and it is now used mainly as a dam for breeding large mules. But the record-breakers are the hybrid offspring of Belgian Brabant mares and American Mammoth jacks:

APOLLO
19.1 hh (199.5 cm) / 2,200 lb (998 kg)

ANAK
18.3 hh (190.5 cm) / 2,100 lb
(952.2 kg)

Apollo was born in Tennessee in
1977, Anak in Kentucky in 1976.

HISTORIC MULES

Mules have a very long history: they
are often portrayed in
Mesopotamian art, especially during
the first millennium BC, and they
were known in western Asia by
2500 BC. There is a tomb painting
from Thebes (c. 1400 BC) with a pair
of animals looking very like
hinnies, drawing a two-wheeled
vehicle with no sign of reins and
with the 'charioteer' facing
backwards; they have strongly
marked shoulder stripes, small ears
and tufted tails. There are
beautifully carved Assyrian reliefs
from Ashurbanipa's palace at
Nineveh and they include a strong
perky mule laden with hunting
equipment: every detail of its
harness is clear, and the end of its
tail is plaited into a loop.

But mules really came into their
own in Roman times, when their
roles were many: they were ridden,
they carried the army's baggage,
they drew carts and worked to the
plough on the farm, for example.
The Romans brought mules to
Britain and knew a great deal about
mule-breeding: they even invented
a mating machine to help the
always shorter jackass to cope with
his mare – he used a sloping wooden
cage to which the poor mare was
firmly harnessed!

In Britain in later centuries, mule
breeding became more profitable
than donkey breeding and was
centred in the New Forest,
conveniently close to
Southampton's docks so that the
young mules could be shipped to
America. George Washington was
the first American to appreciate the
real value of the mule in a huge

undeveloped new world, and it is to
him that the mule owes its ubiquity
in that country. By 1892 there were
several million mules in the United
States.

BRITISH ARMY MULES

The British Army, like the Romans
before them, fully appreciated the
virtues of the mule and considerable
use was made of pack-mules in the
First World War. After the war an
Englishman who had learned to
love the army mules found a new
role for them in peace and set
himself up in France as a most
successful contractor with a team of
mules for ploughing.

In 1923 the War Office said: 'Of
all pack animals, the mule is the
favourite, and although frequently
employed as a draught or riding
animal, it is as a pack carrier that he
is known best. He is capable of great
endurance, tolerates thirst well, can
put up with changes of climate and
food, and is not fastidious regarding
the latter. The shape of his back
makes it easy to fit him with a
saddle, while the toughness of his
hide helps to preserve it from galls.
Mules are usually cheerful,
intelligent animals, appreciate
proper handling, and resent
violence. They are particularly free
kickers, often shy with strangers,
and touchy about the head and ears;
but with attendants that understand
them, they are by no means
troublesome, and easy to look after
and keep in condition. Their one
drawback from a military
standpoint is their liability to
stampede under fire.'

The pace of mule transport was
3–4 miles an hour: the mule was a
quick walker, and a short-stepping,
active pace was preferable to a long
stride as being less likely to shift the
load on its back. American mule
trains, which travelled quite
independently once loaded by
following a 'bell' mare, could move
at an amble or jog if required and

Indian with war mule, 1915. (Billie Love)

were reputed to cover as much as a hundred miles in a day.

MULE SENSE

One of the characteristics of mules is their cautiousness and uncanny sense of danger: they are certainly not fools, and much of their 'obstinacy' is due to their fine sense of self-preservation. It has been said that 'a mule will never starve whilst he has a tail': he has no respect for boundaries and soon migrates if he finds the food on this side of the fence is scarce or unpalatable. The Army motto was, 'Keep their larder full' – it would be cheaper to do so than continually compensate allotment holders!

FAMOUS MULES

CROMPTON'S MULE was the spinning jenny, invented by Samuel Crompton in 1779. It was so called because it was 'a kind of mixture of machinery between the warp-machine of Mr Arkwright and the woof-machine or hand-jenny of Mr Hargrave' and poor Crompton derived little benefit from his toy: it was immediately pirated.

DINAH was the mule in the 1920 *Our Gang* series. She was harnessed within a bottomless bus and lured forwards by an open feed box on the front of the vehicle. In place of a tooting whistle, the driver pulled a string attached to a feather duster which tickled the mule and made her bray.

FADDA was Mohammed's white mule.

FRANCIS was a 'talking' mule first seen in a 1950 film (*Francis*) based on a novel, and there were several sequels including one co-starring Mickey Rooney in 1956. In 1951 Francis received the first Patsy (Picture Animal Top Star of the Year) from the American Humane Association.

MUFFIN was almost the first character on children's television in Britain. The first children's programme *For the Children*, in 1946, featured the Hogarth Puppet Circus and included Fred Woodward as Hank the Mule. Annette Mills (John Mills' sister) and Miller Jones changed the concept to a routine of songs with puppets performing on top of the accompanying piano, and the clumping, spotted Muffin was born.

THE POPE'S MULE was a character in Daudet's *Lettres de mon moulin* (1866): she was given a daily drink of wine by Pope Boniface but her happy life was ruined by a new groom, Tistet Vedene, who once humiliated her by forcing her to climb a bell tower from which she was then lowered in ropes. She had her revenge a few years later, kicking him so violently that all that remained of him was 'a whirlwind of blond dust'.

THALES' MULE, in Michel de Montaigne's *Essays* (1580), was carrying a load of salt when he stumbled fording a river and discovered that salt dissolved in water. Thereafter, displaying true mule sense, he made a habit of falling into streams to lighten his load. His master, Thales of Miletus, was in reality a Greek philosopher who believed that the origin of all things was water.

TROTTER was an American army mule mascot who was famous as the only mule ever to have mastered four gaits (walk, pace, trot and canter) and to maintain a gait for eight hours or fifty miles. He was also the last Army mule to have a serial number tattooed on his ear and inside his lower lip. He was a mascot from 1957 to 1972, coming from Colorado's Fort Carson, and when he retired from West Point he stayed on a farm in Otisville, New York, dying in 1981 at the age of 51.

ONAGERS

The Greek word *hemionos* means mule: literally, it means half-ass

(*hemi* for half, *onos* for ass). The word onager combines ass (*onos*) with wild (*agrios*), hence wild ass. Whether you call it hemione, hemionus or onager in English, it is the Asiatic wild ass and it also goes by other names like kiang, kulan and dzigghetai. Whatever it is, it is not a donkey, which originated from the African wild ass and not from the Asian.

ONAGER-MATOPOEIA

THE ONAGER (*Equus hemionus*), also known as the Asian wild ass, half-ass or hemione, is a pale reddish-brown animal with paler underparts and darker mane and back-stripe; its coat is more yellowish in winter. It is generally larger than the African ass; it has big round hooves and is more like a horse than an ass. Its subspecies include:

Equus hemionus hemionus and *E.h. luteus*, known as kulan, Mongolian wild ass, Kirgiz kulan, chigetai, chiggetai, djigitai, dzeggetai, dzhiggetai, dziggetai, tchikhitei (from the Mongolian 'long-eared'– tchikhi means ear).

E.h. hemippus, known as achdari, akhdari, Mesopotamian onager, Syrian onager, Syrian wild ass or *hemippe de Syrie* – it became extinct in the early 20th century.

E.h. khur, known as Indian wild ass, Baluchi wild ass, ghor khar, Indian onager or khur.

E.h. kulan, known as kulan, koulan, kulon or Transcaspian onager.

E.h. onager, known as Iranian or Persian onager, Persian wild ass or ghor-khar.

THE KIANG (*Equus kiang*), also known as the kyang or Asian wild ass, is a dark red-brown species with white underparts and a white patch behind its shoulder.

THE BENDERI of southern Iran was originally an onager crossed with the Iranian ass.

ANCIENT ONAGERS

There is some doubt about whether or not there were really some onager×donkey hybrids in ancient times or whether the onagers have ever been truly domesticated. They have always been hunted, for food (their meat used to be a relatively important source of food) and for sport, which might be why they have maintained their Roman reputation for being too nervous and bad-tempered to be tamed!

Ancient art depicts animals which might be ass/onager hybrids, for example in a battle scene known as the Standard of Ur on a hollow box covered with mosaics, excavated by Sir Leonard Woolley in southern Babylonia from the royal cemetery of Ur and dated to about 2500 BC. Wild onagers are commonly depicted in ancient art and there is a lovable one on a rein ring from the grave of Queen Puabi, again from Ur in Iraq and of a similar date.

There was an ancient military engine called an onager: it was used to hurl huge stones, which does not seem a very likely role for a wild ass!

Onager on a rein ring from the grave of Queen Puabi of Iraq. (British Museum)

ZEBRASS male zebra×female ass
ZEBRINNY male horse×female zebra
ZEBRONKEY or ZEEDONK an American experiment!
ZEBRULE or ZEBRULA male zebra×female horse
ZEBRA CROSSING pedestrian×Belisha beacon

UNADULTERATED ZEBRAS

THE PLAINS ZEBRA or Common zebra (*Equus burchelli*) of the East African savanna and grasslands tends to look fat, short-legged and dumpy, weighing about 520 lb (235 kg). It is the only plentiful zebra species.

GREVY'S ZEBRA or the Imperial zebra (*Equus grevyi*) of Ethiopia, Somalia and northern Kenya on subdesert steppe and arid shrubby grassland, looks rather like a striped mule with a long, narrow head and

ZEBRAS

The zebras are found only on the African continent in the wild. They are striped horses: it is likely that the equids come from a striped ancestor, and there are hints of this in the 'zebra marks' seen on the legs of some horses and ponies. Although one of the zebra species became extinct a hundred years ago, the other three are still hanging on either in captivity or in the wild, and there have also been several attempts to breed hybrids:

The zebra in three different guises: a) *the Queen's female zebra, 1762;* b) *an early engraving by Stubbs;* c) *a more recent photograph.* (Hulton)

broad, prominent ears; it weighs about 900 lb (405 kg) and is an endangered species.

THE MOUNTAIN ZEBRA (*Equus zebra*) of south-west Africa's mountain grasslands, is thinner and sleeker than the Plains zebra but with a dewlap under its neck; it weighs about 570 lb (260 kg) and is considered a vulnerable species.

THE QUAGGA (*Equus quagga*) of South Africa was yellowish brown with stripes on its head, neck and forebody only; it was exterminated in the 1880s.

Zebras in general are active, noisy and bold: they do not try and hide themselves and seem content to be conspicuous. Some people say they can never be tamed, though there are stories to the contrary.

ZOO ZEBRAS

The animals very occasionally featured in Italian menageries of the 15th and 16th centuries as rarities, but it was the 'scientific' zoological gardens of the 19th century where zebras became more familiar to the general public, and the first animal portrait painted by the famous horse artist George Stubbs was of a zebra. The French zoologist Daubenton, at the Jardin d'Acclimatation in Paris, tried to help the zebra adapt to a European habitat in order that a new draught and pack animal might be available which would be 'stronger than the donkey and, even when naked, more beautiful than the most splendidly bridled horse'. But in the long term he was no more successful than Geoffrey Saint-Hilaire, Bonaparte's court zoologist in the early years of the 19th century, who had tried to domesticate the onager.

Let's be content with those we have already tamed, shamed and subjugated – let the wild run free, and let there be a wilderness for them to live in.

THE UNICORN

The fabulous unicorn has a very ancient history. Unicorn-like animals are found in hieroglyphic inscriptions of the land of Osiris and there is a chequerboard lion and unicorn dating back to 3500 BC. A Romano-Egyptian papyrus in the British Museum shows the lion and the unicorn playing draughts and in that eternal game the lion, representing summer, will always win over the unicorn of spring.

The animal was described in literature in 400 BC by Ctesias and was always a solitary creature, living under the special protection of the moon goddess Diana and communing with the stars and the sky. The Romans and Greeks believed that real unicorns existed in India but it is more likely that the original concept came from an African animal – the oryx, an antelope with two long, straight, parallel horns which, in profile, often appear to be one. The oryx is used as a symbol in countries like Bahrain and Oman.

The Greeks, whose ancient coins displayed the fabled beast, thought that the Indian unicorn was a very dangerous animal: it could be captured only by a virgin, and it would peacefully lay its head in her lap. Thus the white horned horse became, by association, a symbol of purity and virginity and the protector of virtue.

ALICORN

Its single horn had many a magical power ascribed to it, of course. It was said that a unicorn could detect with the tip of its horn whether a liquid contained poison, and that the horn was an antidote to poison. Many medieval collectors had fragments of unicorn horn, known as alicorn, especially royalty. Elizabeth I's inventory of royal jewels included a piece and a German traveller later saw 'a horn